Statistical

Measures:

A Programmed Text

CENTRAL TENDENCY

DISPERSION

CORRELATION

Frank F. Gorow

Statistical Measures:

A Programmed Text

CENTRAL TENDENCY, DISPERSION, CORRELATION

By Frank F. Gorow

LONG BEACH STATE COLLEGE

 Chandler Publishing Company

SAN FRANCISCO

STATISTICAL MEASURES

Chandler Publications in

EDUCATIONAL PSYCHOLOGY

DAVID G. RYANS, *Editor*

Preface

Statistical Measures: A Programmed Text is a scrambled text-book containing branching programs for learning to compute the statistics which are usually included in a course in tests and measurements for prospective secondary-school teachers. It was developed and tested in connection with the author's courses at Long Beach State College, then further tested, criticized, and revised by Professor H. Paul Kelley at the University of Texas, and thereafter revised for this publication.

The use of this scrambled and programmed material permitted a reduction of about a third in the class time assigned to the statistics unit; the time gained was used for an additional topic introduced into the course.

The emphasis in *Statistical Measures* is put on *the student learning* rather than on *the instructor teaching*. The scrambled sequence of the sections in this book prevents a student's uncomprehendingly and unresponsively groping through the pages. He must respond; he can go from one section to the next only as the result of a response that he makes after reading. If that response is wrong, he is soon back where he started; if and when it is correct, he progresses. If he needs special guidance, the program provides it before sending him back to resume his progress. If he does not need special guidance, he will not have his time absorbed or his attention diluted by reading sections that he does not need to study. The instructor is freed to give individual help to students who need it. He is also enabled to concentrate his teaching on insights and orientations that lie beyond the stated objectives of a book on how to compute statistics.

Two familiar components of traditional textbooks will not be found in *Statistical Measures*. There is no index. There are no running heads to indicate the subject matter of the successive pages. The omission of these is calculated and intended. This book is for study—not for reference, not for consultation to locate details of information out of context. Review is provided for, nevertheless—*in context*. At places in the text suggestions for review are made. And a student who chooses to review a topic can locate in the table of contents the point at which his review can best begin.

To Professor H. Paul Kelley the author is sincerely and especially appreciative. Professor Kelley gave this book a thorough review, exhaustive testing, and candid criticism—which have been used in the shaping of the final result.

Contents

STATISTICAL MEASURES

How This Book Works

The material in *Statistical Measures* is organized into numbered sections. Most sections correspond to steps in learning how to compute simple statistics. By following the steps as they are presented, you will learn.

You are to read the instructions and follow the steps. You do *not* read this book from section 1 through sections 2 and 3 and so on to the end. What you read after section 1 depends on your answer to a question in this section; you may be sent to section 4 or to section 8. Only by answering can you know what your next step is. Thus you will be tested at almost every step; the testing is built into the book. When you make a mistake (or answer a question incorrectly), you will be informed promptly of your error and guided in correcting it. You will then perform the step correctly and proceed to the next step.

If you attempt to read everything in this book you may become badly confused. Some sections are intended to help people who make certain mistakes and unless you make these mistakes these sections are of no use to you. Hence you should just follow the directions and read the numbered sections to which you are referred. *Don't read the other sections!*

The numbered sections are grouped in three parts, having to do with small sets of scores, large sets of scores, and measures of relationship. Each part has a page of introductory material which you may usefully read before starting to work on the numbered section at the beginning of the part.

This book is too small to tell everything about the vast field of statistics. You may want to consult, while you are studying this book or afterwards, a few useful references; there is a list of them in the appendix. You may want a summary of the contents of this book; there is a summary and a set of formulas in an appendix. You may want some information about the uses of the statistics you will learn to compute; a brief example of the interpretation of test data is also given in an appendix.

Now you are ready to begin studying Part One. Begin with section 1, or with the introductory material on the page that precedes section 1.

Part One

SMALL SETS OF SCORES

In Part One of this book you will work with small sets of scores and develop two types of statistics:

> measures of central tendency (also called averages)
> measures of dispersion (also called measures of variability or spread)

Both kinds of measures are needed to summarize and interpret a set of test scores. These are the kinds of statistics that teachers use most frequently.

The word *average* is in the vocabulary of most adults, but it is a loose term. As the word is often used, the average is the *arithmetic mean,* more simply the *mean*, found by adding all the scores in a set and dividing the sum by the number of scores. Another statistic, sometimes miscalled an average, is the *mid-score*, the *mid-point* of a set of scores, which is called the *median*. A third statistic of this general type is the *mode*—the most frequently occurring score, in a sense the most popular score. There are still others, some of which are not to be studied in this book. They will be called *measures of central tendency*, since *average* can be a misleading term.

Several *measures of dispersion,* variability, or spread can be obtained from a small set of test scores. Part I will deal with two of them: the *range* and the *standard deviation*. The *range* is the simpler, being merely the spread including the highest and lowest scores. The *standard deviation* is more complicated; it takes into account the amount by which each score differs or deviates from the mean.

It needs to be made clear that statistics is best applied to large sets of scores. Statisticians speak of *universes* or *populations* of data. When you apply statistical methods of analysis to small sets of data you sometimes get into anomalies. The value of Part One, dealing as it does with small sets of scores, is to introduce basic ideas and procedures that you will thereby understand when you apply them to large sets of scores.

At the end of Part One, in a Conclusion and Review, the qualities and uses of the several measures are discussed and compared.

The Mean: A Measure of Central Tendency

1 Suppose we have given a test to a class and wish to "summarize" the scores of the individuals who took it.

First, we find the measures of central tendency.

Here are the scores for one class:

29	26	34	31	24	29	37	35
36	30	30	29	35	31	28	22
35	32						

To find the *arithmetic* mean, or mean, we add all the scores and divide by the number of scores.

Do we need to place them in order of size?

If you answer "yes," see section 4.

If your answer is "no," turn to section 8.

2 How many scores are in the set in section 1?

If you counted 17, see section 9.

If your count is 18, turn to section 5.

If 19 is your count, proceed to section 7.

3 What is the *sum* of the scores in section 1?

If your sum is 553, see section 10.

A sum of 554 leads you to section 6.

If 563 is your sum, turn to section 14.

And if your sum is any other number see section 17.

4 If you wish merely to add the numbers, they need not be in order of size, but if you are looking ahead to the *median* and the *mode* of the scores, you have a head start by arranging them in order of size as you copy them on your paper. Your answer is satisfactory.

Turn to section 2.

5 Counting is simple, but mistakes can occur easily. Your count is correct, so proceed with section 3.

6 You have made an error. To avoid mistakes like this, always check your work. How? Add the columns from the top down; then add them from the bottom up. Two answers that differ indicate an error. Two answers that are the same *may* be correct.

Return to section 3 and try again. This time, check your work.

7 Counting is an important process in statistics and errors are easy to make with a large number of scores. But you made a mistake with a small number of scores.

Return to section 2 and count the scores again.

8 Correct. You need not arrange scores in order of size to find the *mean*.

However, you will need to place the scores in order of size to determine the other measures, so you save time by arranging them in order of size as you copy them.

Turn now to section 2.

9 Counting is an important process in statistics, and errors are easy to make when you have a large number of scores. But you made a mistake with a small number of scores.

Return to section 2 and count the scores again.

10   You are correct; the sum of the scores is 553.

To determine the mean, divide the *sum* of the scores by the *number* of scores. Since you have the correct sum and number, you should find the mean without difficulty.

Compute the mean and proceed to section 13.

11   Now, where are you?

You found a measure of central tendency and computed to *four* decimal places. Why go to all that work? Test scores are not perfectly precise measures, so why try for a high degree of precision in computing statistics of them?

See section 21 for a discussion of decimal places.

12   If you changed your answer after looking at the choices, you risked confusing yourself. To see how, turn to section 20.

If you *computed* this mean, proceed to section 18.

13   The arithmetic mean of the set of scores is what? That is,

$$Mn = \text{---} ? \text{---}.$$

If your answer is 30.7222, see section 12.
If your answer is 30, proceed to section 15.
The answer 30.7 leads you to section 19.
Any other answer sends you to section 16.

14   You have made a mistake. Did you check your addition? How?

Try adding the columns twice, once down and once up; the two answers should be the same.

Return to section 3 and add the scores again. And check your addition.

15   Can you estimate whether the next decimal number will be larger or smaller than 5? It makes a difference in your answer, so return to section 13 and correct your answer (the decimal number). Then proceed as directed on the basis of your new answer.

16   You have one of the "other" answers.

If you wrote 30.72, you are technically correct. A better answer is 30.7; for the reason, see section 21.

If you have 31, you found the score which is closest to the mean. Carrying the mean to one decimal place has an advantage, however. For the reason, see section 21.

If you have any other number, you'd better return to section 13 and check your division. Remember, you must have the correct answer before continuing.

17   "Any other number" includes all possible wrong sums, of which you seem to have found one.

Did you check your addition by adding the columns twice, once up and once down?

Return to section 3 and try again.

18   If you tried to keep dividing until "it comes out even," you have missed the point of computing the *mean* of a set of scores.

For a discussion of decimal places, see section 21.

19   How did you get this answer?

It is correct, but you need to know why. See section 21.

20 It sometimes sends you on a wild goose chase, like this one, in which you learn very little because you know you were kidding yourself.

It might even lead you away from the problem. To get back on the track, turn to section 11.

21 Why are measures of central tendency computed to one and only one decimal place?

Because we are dealing with scores which are whole numbers and we therefore need only one decimal place to establish the location of any measure among these scores. The mean (or the median) of a set of whole-number scores usually falls between two scores. If it is computed as 30.7, that figure locates it between 30 and 31, and there is no need to refine the computation by carrying it to 30.7222, since this refinement will not move it out from between 30 and 31.

You have computed the mean of a set of test scores. You may review the steps of the process in sections 1, 2, and 10.

The next series, which concerns the *median*, begins with section 22.

The Median: A Measure of Central Tendency

22   The *median* is the correct name for the mid-score or the mid-point of a set of scores. *Median* is abbreviated *Md*.

To find this measure of central tendency, first place the scores in order of size (if you have not already done so).

The scores given in section 1 are:

29	26	34	31	24	29	37	35
36	30	30	29	35	31	28	22
35	32						

After arranging the scores in order of size, count up half-way from the bottom score (or half-way down from the top) to locate the mid-point or median.

If you find the median is 30, see section 24.

If your median is 30½, refer to section 28.

A median of 30.5 leads you to section 30.

If your median is 31, see section 26.

And, if you have still a different number, see section 25.

23   Not 63. There were 10 scores; there must be 5 scores above the median and 5 scores below the median.

Counting up, beginning with the smallest score, the fifth score is 62 and the sixth is 63. The median is half-way between the fifth and sixth scores.

With an *even number* of scores, the median is half-way between the two scores in the middle.

Try again in section 24.

24   You want the mid-point. You don't have it, for 7 scores are lower than 30 and 9 scores are higher.

Try finding the median of this set of scores:

63   67   58   64   59   65   60   63   61   62

First, place the scores in order of size, the largest down to the smallest.

Second, find how many scores there are.

Third, count up half-way, beginning with the smallest score. If you find the median of the scores is:

     62—then see section 27.
     62.5—then see section 29.
     63—then see section 23.

25   You have still a different number for the median; your answer is not correct.

How many scores were there? Do you have the scores listed in order of size? The mid-point is half-way from the bottom—or from the top.

Return to section 22 and try again.

26   You want the mid-point. You don't have it.
Try finding the median of this series:

58   67   63   60   69   56   65   61   70   62

First, place the scores in order of size, the largest down to the smallest.

Next, find how many scores there are.

Last, count up half-way, beginning with the smallest score.

If you find the median of these scores is:

      62—then see section 27.
      62.5—then see section 29.
      63—then see section 23.

27   Not 62. There were 10 scores; there must be 5 scores above the median and 5 scores below the median.

Counting up from the smallest score, the fifth score is 62 and the sixth is 63. The median is half-way between the fifth and sixth scores.

With an *even number* of scores, the median is half-way between the two scores in the middle.

Try again in section 26.

28 You have the right idea and the right answer. However, decimals are preferable to fractions in statistical measures.

Change your ½ to .5 and proceed to section 30.

29 You are correct. Now return to section 22 and find the median of the scores in that section.

30   Correct. The median is half-way between two scores when there is an even number of scores and the two middle scores are not of the same size. With an odd number of scores, the median is the middle score.

You have located the *point* which divides the set of scores into two equal parts. It is the median, a measure of central tendency. It may also be called the mid-point of a set of scores.

The median may be hidden in a number of scores of the same size, as in the set:

    57   58   60   60   61   62   62   62   64
    67   68

Here 62 is the median: half the scores are at or above 62 and half the scores are at or below 62. This kind of absurdity often occurs, and it is one reason why small sets of scores are not truly susceptible of statistical analysis; statistics deals best with large sets of scores.

For a third measure of central tendency, proceed to section 31.

The Mode: A Measure of Central Tendency

31 The *mode* is the score which occurs with the greatest frequency—in a sense, the most popular score. *Mode* is abbreviated *Mo*. It requires no computation but is determined by inspection.

29	26	34	31	24	29	37	35	36
30	30	29	35	31	28	22	35	32

Above is the original list of scores (as in section 1 or section 22). Find the mode.

$$Mo = — ? —.$$

If you found $Mo = 35$, see section 33.
A mode of 29 leads you to section 35.
If you found any other number, you should look again.
And, if you could not find a mode, see section 34.

32 Quite right. While one score appears slightly more frequently than any other, there is no score which definitely is the most popular. A mode must be well-defined to be useful; that is, one score should stand out from all others because it occurs most often. The mode is less useful to teachers than the other measures of central tendency.

Why less useful? Consider the set of scores in section 34. Double it by repeating each score; then you have:

16	16	18	18	16	16	13	13
15	15	17	17	26	26	21	21
19	19	23	23	15	15	13	13
17	17	9	9	19	19	16	16

Now, the largest group of scores is six for score 16, in contrast to four for scores 13, 15, 17, and 19. Six in comparison to four is relatively well defined. Perhaps 16 is a mode? A measure that can shift in this fashion is scarcely more useful than a rubber tape measure.

Proceed now to section 37.

33 You say 35 is the mode. But there is another score with the same frequency, hence 35 cannot be *the* mode.

Return to section 31 and look again.

34 In this case there are two scores which occur more frequently than any others. You cannot see that either is a mode.

Look at this set of scores:

16	18	16	13	15	17	26	21
19	23	15	13	17	9	19	16

Is there a mode?

If you answer "yes," see section 36.

If your answer is "no," turn to section 32.

35 You say 29 is the mode. However, there is another score with the same frequency, hence 29 cannot be *the* mode.

Return to section 31 and look again.

36   "Yes" is the wrong answer.

No score in this set should be called a mode. While it is true that one score occurs slightly more frequently than any other, this score does not stand out as being definitely more popular than any other. To be useful, a mode should be well-defined; that is, it should appear much more frequently than any other scores.

Return to section 34, inspect the scores again, and try for the correct answer.

Three Measures of Central Tendency

37   You have computed or found three measures of central tendency of a set of scores, those given in section 1.

We can summarize the central tendency of these scores by reporting:

mean (or "arithmetic average") = — ? —
median (or mid-point) = — ? —
mode = — ? —

Your values should be correct.
Turn to section 38 to make sure.

38   The measures of central tendency of the given scores are:

    mean = 30.7
    median = 30.5
    mode = none well defined

Why do we have three different measures of the same kind? Is one a better measure of central tendency than the others?

Recall the procedure for finding each: they represent three different aspects of central tendency. The *mode* is significant only when a large number of students made a perfect score or some other score on a test. The *median* is a stable measure, not influenced by extreme high or low scores. However, it is a point which separates the high and low scores and is not a true average. The *mean* is influenced by scores which are extreme (compared to the median) and which thereby raise the average or lower it. One must often compute both the median and the mean to find out whether or not they differ enough to suggest an imbalance of high and low scores.

The measure of choice is the one that most fairly represents central tendency. If a very hard test were given, such that many students received zero scores, only the mode would have meaning. On an easy test with many high scores—but with a few trailing far below most of the scores—these few extremely low scores would depress the mean and give a distorted view of the class average; the median would more fairly represent the central tendency. The mean is ordinarily the most useful of these measures, since it represents the "average" of a set of scores. Only when the distribution of scores makes the mean suspect as a fair measure would the median or the mode be more useful.

If you wish to review the steps in finding the three measures of central tendency:

    mean: sections 1, 2, 3, 10
    median: sections 22, 30
    mode: sections 31, 34, 32

You are now ready to compute measures of dispersion or spread.

Proceed to section 39.

The Range: A Measure of Dispersion

39   Measures of central tendency do not tell the whole story of a set of test scores. We need to know how much variation there is, how much the scores spread out, how they are dispersed.

The simplest and easiest-to-find measure of dispersion, variability, or spread is the *range,* represented by the letter R.

It is the difference between the highest score and the lowest score, *plus one.*

Here is the set of scores for which you have already found measures of central tendency. Find the range of the same scores.

29	26	34	31	24	29	37	35	36
30	30	29	35	31	28	22	35	32

$R = $ — ? —

If you found $R = 15$, turn to section 41.
If your range is 16, see section 40.
And if you have any other number, look again.

40 Your answer is correct: $R = 16$.

Most textbooks on statistics define *range* as "the difference between the highest and the lowest scores, plus one." Notice that the difference between the extreme scores does not include the entire range. For example:

$$20 - 17 = 3$$

But the range includes the numbers 17, 18, 19, 20—four numbers. Hence the range is 4. The range is 1 more than the difference between the extreme scores; thus:

$$\text{(highest score)} - \text{(lowest score)} + 1 = \text{range}$$

Range is a measure of the dispersion, variability, or spread of scores. How good or how useful is range? This question is discussed in section 42.

41 You found the difference between the highest and lowest scores, but your answer does not include all of the possible scores. For example: in the set of numbers 3, 4, 5, 6, 7, the difference between the highest and the lowest is 4 (that is, $7 - 3$), but there are *five* scores.

The range is the number of possible score values, including the largest and smallest. Return to section 39 for the definition of range; then correct your answer.

42   The range depends on two scores only—the most extreme high and the most extreme low; range ignores the rest. Though some scores between the extremes may occur twice or oftener and though some numbers between the extremes may not occur as scores, range is unaffected by these facts and does not show them. It may, therefore, give an incomplete impression about the dispersion or spread of the scores.

For example, the highest and lowest scores on a 100-item test might be 95 and 20, giving a range of 76. This range suggests a very large spread of the scores. But what of the other scores? Are they also spread out or are they bunched near the middle?

Because the range is based upon the two extreme scores, ignoring all others, it is considered a poor measure of dispersion. It might be improved by eliminating the extreme scores and finding the range of the others; or by cutting off the top fourth and the bottom fourth of the scores and finding the range of the middle half (which is the *quartile range*).

A more useful measure of spread takes into account every score and its variation from the measure of central tendency.

Proceed to section 43.

The Standard Deviation: A Measure of Dispersion

43   A measure of dispersion that takes into account the variation or deviation of *every* score from the mean score is the *standard deviation*. It is the most useful and most reliable measure of variability, spread, or dispersion. The reasons why cannot be presented until after you have studied the computation. The symbol for standard deviation is σ (the Greek lowercase letter sigma).

The standard deviation is, by definition, the square root of the mean of the squares of the deviations of scores from the mean score. To compute the standard deviation, you need to follow a series of steps in this order:

Find the deviations of scores from the mean score.	37	
	36	
Find the squares of these deviations.	35	
Find the mean of these squares.	35	
(Take their sum and divide it by *N,* the	35	
number of scores.)	34	
Find the square root of this mean.	32	deviation 1
	31	deviation 0
Here again is the set of scores for	31	deviation 0
which you have found range and meas-	30	deviation 1
ures of central tendency, arrayed in	30	deviation 1
order of size. What is its standard devi-	29	
ation, that is, its σ?	29	
	29	
	28	
	26	
	24	
	22	

To find the σ of this set of scores, first locate the score nearest to the mean and mark it 0, because it does not deviate or

33   § **43**

43 differ from the mean. (Strictly speaking, the scores of 31 deviate by 0.3 from the mean, which was 30.7. But it simplifies the process to use whole numbers. Your σ will be almost, but probably not exactly, the same as the σ computed from the more precise deviation values.)

The score 32 differs by 1 and the score 30 likewise differs from the mean of 31. (The deviations of the scores below the mean are negative numbers, but you need not be concerned with $+$ and $-$ signs in this process because you will not add the deviations.)

Mark each of the scores with its deviation from 31 (using whole numbers.) Write the deviations in a column next to the scores and label this column d.

As a check on your accuracy, note the deviation you have computed for the largest score, 37.

If it is 6, turn to section 45.

If it is 7, see section 47.

If you have any other number for this deviation, return to the beginning of the explanation in the paragraph that follows the array of scores in this section.

44 Your quotient is not correct.

Did you divide 297 (that is, Σd^2) by 18 (that is, by N)?

Return to section 48 and correct your answer.

45 Correct. The score of 37 deviates from the mean of 31 by 6.

You have made a column of the deviations from the mean of the scores given in section 43.

The next step is to *square* each deviation. Make a column of the squares and label it d^2.

Next, add the numbers in the d^2 column. This sum is "Σd^2." The Greek letter Σ (capital sigma) represents "the sum of," hence Σd^2 means "the sum of the squares of the deviations."

$$\Sigma d^2 = \underline{\quad} ? \underline{\quad}$$

If your sum is 298, see section 46.

If you obtained 297, see section 48.

If you have any other number for Σd^2, check your addition.

46   You have made an error, or errors.

Return to section 45 and check your addition of the d^2 column. If you get a new figure for Σd^2, then proceed as instructed with respect to this figure.

But you may find your addition correct. If so, you must look for your error in an earlier computation. So check your computations of d^2. If you find one or more of them wrong, put the correct figure in the d^2 column and add this corrected column to find Σd^2; then proceed as instructed with respect to this figure at the end of section 45.

But you may find your d^2 values correct for your d values; if so, you may have made an error in computing d values in section 43. So compute them again; if you find any wrong, then compute the corresponding d^2 again, add the corrected d^2 column to get Σd^2, and proceed as instructed with respect to this Σd^2 at the end of section 45.

47   No, your computed deviation is incorrect. The deviation of 37 from the mean of 31 is 6 (for $37 - 31 = 6$).

Return to section 43 and check *all* of your deviations. (Remember the deviation is the difference between the score and the mean score.)

48   Correct. In section 43, you found Σd^2, the sum of the deviations, to be 297.

Next, divide Σd^2 by N, the number of scores.

$$\frac{\Sigma d^2}{N} = \;—\; ? \;—$$

If your quotient is 16.5, see section 49.
If you found a quotient of 17.5, turn to section 44.

49   Correct. You found:

$$\frac{\Sigma d^2}{N} = \frac{297}{18} = 16.5$$

The last step in computing the standard deviation is to find the square root of this quotient.

There are several ways of finding square roots:

(1) You learned one method in elementary school; if this is familiar, use it.

(2) Perhaps the easiest way is to use a slide rule IF you have one and know how to use it.

(3) Some statistics books have numerical tables, including a table of square roots. If you do not have a table of square roots, and cannot use the first two methods, you may be forced to try method 4, which follows.

(4) The method of approximation requires only simple division. There are just three steps:

    (a) Guess the square root (a rough guess).
    (b) Divide the number by your guess.
    (c) Take the mean of the quotient and the divisor.

This mean gives the approximate square root of the number. (It may be necessary to repeat the whole process one or more times if the new estimate of the square root differs from the original guess by more than 0.1. If the process is repeated, the new estimate is used as the guess for the repetition.)

Using any method your prefer, find the square root of 16.5. Check your result in section 51.

50   The standard deviation, symbol σ, is a measure of dispersion or spread of a set of scores. The range is a similar measure but the two differ greatly. The range is always a large number and depends upon the two extreme scores, ignoring the rest. The range thus cannot fairly represent the spread of a set of scores; its use lies in determining the *extent* of spread so that the scores may be grouped.

The standard deviation represents the spread of all the scores and is a better measure than the range. More will be said about its usefulness later.

How do measures of central tendency and of spread fit together? Why do we compute the statistics of a set of scores?

Continue with section 52.

51   You should have found the square root of 16.5 to be 4.06, which rounds to 4.1.

This square root is σ, the standard deviation of the 18 scores. Here is a review of the steps in computing σ:

(1) Place the scores in order of size.

(2) Compute the mean of the scores.

(3) Determine the deviation of each score from the mean, making a d column.

(4) Square each deviation, making a d^2 column.

(5) Find Σd^2, the sum of the squares of the deviations.

(6) Divide Σd^2 by N, the number of scores, to get a quotient.

(7) Take the square root of the quotient.

The formula for σ is

$$\sqrt{\frac{\Sigma d^2}{N}} \, .$$

Now that you have computed σ, what does it mean? Proceed to section 50.

The Relation of the Measures

52 You have now computed or found five measures of a set of scores: the mean, median, mode, range, and standard deviation.

You have answered the questions: "What is the average score?" and "How much dispersion or spread do the scores show?"

We *summarize* a set of scores by reporting a measure of central tendency and a measure of dispersion.

Such a pair of measures must be *related* or computed by similar processes. Thus the median and the range are paired because they represent the middle and end *points* of a set of scores. Similarly, the mean and the standard deviation are paired because both take into account every score and the deviations are taken from the mean as average, not the median of the scores.

To summarize the set of 18 test scores, we can report a median of 30.5 and a range of 16. We can also report a mean of 30.7 and a standard deviation of 4.1.

The interpretation of such statistical information is not easy because there are no absolutes, no physical dimensions, no standards for comparison. We report a class average—but is it high or is it low? The question cannot be answered without comparison to the average of some other group of students or to an arbitrarily chosen standard. Similarly, the standard deviation of the scores on one set of test papers may be greater or less than that of another set, but without a comparison we cannot interpret a measure of dispersion as being high or low. If we were to give a test once and never again there would be little value in its statistics. When we wish to compare one class with another or to compare the test performance this year and last, we need a summary of each test for comparison. When we revise a test in an effort to improve it, we need statistics for comparison.

These uses of test statistics are in addition to the usual com-

52 parisons of the performance of each student with his class or with some other comparison group. Here standard deviation is useful: How far above or below the class average is a given test score? With the mean and the standard deviation, a set of *standard scores* can be prepared to make possible the combining of scores on several tests or other measures of performance. Further interpretation of central tendency and of dispersion will be made in Part Two. Your primary concern now is with the concepts and the computation. Be sure you understand them! If you wish to review:

> The *mean* begins with section 1.
> The *median* begins with section 22.
> The *mode* begins with section 31.
> The *range* begins with section 39.
> The *standard deviation* begins with section 43.

The *computation processes* to be used in Part Two will be different from those you have used. But the *concepts* are the same. The reason for using the different processes has to do with the greater number of scores in the sets; the processes may strike you as far more complex, but if you understand the concepts you will be able to understand the new processes.

Before beginning work with a large set of scores, see if you can remember and apply all that you have learned thus far. Complete one or both of the exercises in the General Assignment, section 54.

53   You should have found the measures of central tendency for the scores in Exercise 1 of section 54 to be:

mean $= 31.4$
median $= 31.5$
mode: none well defined

You should have found the measures of spread for the same set of scores to be:

range $= 23$
standard deviation $= 5.6 = \sigma$

For Exercise 2, you should have found: $Mn = 42.1$, $Md = 43.0$, Mo, none well defined, $R = 18$, $\sigma = 4.9$.

If your answers indicate that you can compute these measures with justified confidence, you are ready to proceed with the study of Part Two: Large Sets of Scores.

Go to section 55. It may be useful to read first the introductory material on the page facing section 55.

General Assignment

54 *Exercise 1.* Given the scores:

| 39 | 36 | 21 | 35 | 28 | 33 | 19 | 35 | 32 | 29 | 41 |
| 24 | 35 | 38 | 30 | 26 | 30 | 38 | 31 | 32 | 28 | 30 |

Find: Three measures of central tendency—the mean, the median, and the mode. Round answers to one decimal place.

Also find: Two measures of dispersion—the range and the standard deviation, rounded to one decimal place.

Exercise 2. Given the scores:

| 44 | 39 | 49 | 46 | 38 | 44 | 48 |
| 32 | 40 | 35 | 42 | 48 | 40 | 44 |

Find: Mean, median, mode, range, standard deviation. Round answers to one decimal place.

If you wish to check your answers, turn to section 53.

After you have completed this assignment, you may proceed with Part Two: Large Sets of Scores.

Part Two

LARGE SETS OF SCORES

Teachers use statistics primarily for summarizing and describing sets of test scores. A measure of central tendency and a measure of dispersion provide a basis for interpreting each individual score; that is, for comparing each score with the performance of the class as a whole or with the performance of some larger group. With a small set of scores, the statistics are computed by working directly with the scores themselves. You have computed statistical measures of a small number of scores—fewer than fifty scores.

If you had several hundred or several thousand scores, you could compute your statistics in the same way. However, you would find the work laborious and subject to computational errors. It is usually more convenient to arrange the scores in groups and to use modified procedures which yield reliable approximations of the basic statistics.

In Part Two you will develop these modified procedures for obtaining the statistics already introduced in Part One, as well as certain additional statistics. The main concern will continue to be with measures of central tendency and of dispersion. The mean and the median are the central-tendency measures most frequently used for grouped scores. The corresponding measures of dispersion are the standard deviation and the quartile deviation.

In the course of working with these most frequently used statistics, you will meet some others—*quartiles, deciles,* and *percentiles*—which are often used in interpreting scores on published or standardized tests in high school and college.

Grouping Data in a Frequency Distribution

55   When a set of scores is so large as to be unwieldy and require laborious computation with a probability of error, it is usually convenient to arrange the scores in groups and to work with the groups instead of the individual scores. The ideal number of groups is usually considered to be 15, with limits set at not fewer than 10 groups and not more than 20. Why are limits set at 10 and 20 groups? What would be the effect of arranging the scores into fewer than 10 groups? What would be the result of an arrangement with more than 20 groups?

Compare your answers with those given in section 57.

56   You say: "Yes, we must know the number of scores." But you are to have about 15 groups. If you have 50 or 60 scores, you will divide them into 15 groups; if the number of scores is 500 or 600, you still divide them into about 15 groups. Thus the *number* of scores is not a factor in deciding how to divide the set of scores into about 15 groups.

Return to section 62 and choose the right answer. The choice should now be easy.

57 The ideal number of score groups is about 15. This number of groups permits the computation of measures of central tendency and of dispersion which are reasonably good approximations of the statistics. With fewer than 10 groups, the grouping is coarse and the resulting statistical values are less precise than is desirable. If the scores are arranged into more than 20 groups, the labor of computation is increased without causing a compensating increase in precision. Hence the general rule is to arrange the scores into approximately 15 groups, with no fewer than 10 nor more than 20 groups.

When you have a large number of test scores and wish to compute the measures of central tendency and of dispersion, the first step is to group the scores. Why should the scores be grouped?

If you say, "Because that's the way the statisticians do it," see section 58.

If you say, "To compute the statistics more easily," see section 62.

58 You say that scores are grouped because statisticians do it. That answer may sound reasonable—but it is not a very good reason!

Return to section 55 and the introduction, reread them, and start over.

59 You selected 2 sizes of score for each group.

Look at it this way: you had 46 possible sizes of score; if you place 2 sizes in each group, you will have 23 groups $(2 \times 23 = 46)$.

That's too many groups—more than you need.

Return to section 60, reread it, and choose another answer.

60 You say: "No, we do not need to know the number of scores"—and you are correct.

With a large number of scores, there will be more scores in each group. With a small number of scores, there will be fewer scores in each group. You do not need to know the number of scores in order to plan the grouping.

You *do* need to know the *range* of the scores; knowing this, you know the number of possible sizes of score, including the largest and the smallest scores.

You divide the range by 15 (a desirable number of groups) and take the nearest whole number. This tells you the number of *sizes* of score to place in each group. (Recall that the symbol *"R"* stands for range.) Use the symbol *"i"* to stand for the number of score sizes in each group.

If you should have a range of 46, how many sizes of score would you place in each group? In symbolic language, if $R = 46$, $i = $ — ? —.

If you say $i = 2$, see section 59.
If you say $i = 3$, see section 64.
If you say $i = 4$, see section 66.
If you don't know, see section 68.

61 You would discard a score size to "come out even."

Come now! You would not discard a student's score!

You had 46 possible sizes of score and, if you are to find any statistic, you must use all of them.

Return to section 64 and try again.

62 Right. Grouping scores usually permits the computation of statistics more easily, and hence with less chance of computational error, than is possible by the methods we previously used with small sets of scores. (However, when a desk calculator is available, the small-set methods may be easier, even with a large number of scores.)

Now, to group a set of scores, do you need to know N (that is, the number of scores)?

If you say yes, see section 56.

If you say no, see section 60.

63   With 82 possible sizes of score, you suggest placing 5 sizes in each group.

Let's check: 82 divided by 5 would give 16 groups and 2 sizes left over for a 17th group. This 17 is more than the ideal number of groups.

Your procedure is correct, however.

82 divided by 15 gives a result which is between 5 and 6; so, we may have 5 sizes or 6 sizes in a group. Which is preferable? Which will produce a number closer to the ideal of 15 groups?

If you think 5 is preferable, reread this section.

If you think 6 is preferable, turn to section 65.

64   You would place 3 sizes of score in each group. Correct: $i = 3$.

$$46 \div 15 = 3 \text{ (with one score size left over)}$$

What will you do with the one left over?

If you would discard it, see section 61.

If you would make another group, see section 69.

If you would include it in one of the other groups, see section 67.

65 With 82 possible sizes of score, you suggest placing 6 sizes in a group.

This decision seems to check out: 82 divided by 15 gives a result which is between 5 and 6; hence *either* is a proper number of sizes in a group.

$82 \div 5 = 16$ groups, with 2 sizes over for a 17th group.
$82 \div 6 = 13$ groups, with 4 sizes over for a 14th group.

Either grouping is satisfactory. However, 14 groups of 6 sizes each is closer to the ideal of 15 groups of score sizes.

Now, to set up the actual groups:

The top group must contain the highest score.

If (for example) you decide to have 2 sizes in a group (that is, if $i = 2$) and the highest score is 65, what sizes of score will be placed in the top group?

If you think 64 and 65, see section 70.

If you think 65 and 66, see section 73.

If you think it doesn't make any difference, see section 76.

66 You would place 4 sizes of score in each group.

Look again.

Remember that you had 46 sizes (or possible sizes).

If you divide 46 by 4, you will have 11 groups (of 4 sizes each) and 2 sizes left over.

Either 11 or 12 is above the lower limit of 10 groups—but comes close to the danger limit of too few groups.

Return to section 60, choose a better answer, and follow the instructions with respect to it.

67 No. You can't include the "extra" score size in one of the other groups.

Every group must contain the same number of sizes of score: 3 sizes, or 2 sizes, or some other number of sizes—never 3 in most and 4 in one.

Now you may be desperate. You don't want to ignore that leftover score size (indeed, you must not). You have just been told you can't include it in one of the other groups, because groups must be equal. Here is a hint: there may be some possible score *sizes* higher or lower than the range of actual *scores;* maybe you can use one or more of these possible score sizes to make a group with the left-over item.*

Return to section 64 and try again.

---

* It is possible, of course, to have scores down to and including zero, and the leftover score may be zero. You cannot include it with one or more imaginary scores below the lowest actual score! You might make a fresh start on the grouping process, using zero as the lowest score, and working up instead of down (adding an extra imaginary score or scores at the top; the extra high scores may even be higher than the highest actually possible score):

68   You don't know how many sizes of score will be in a group.

It may help you to imagine that you have 46 slips of paper, each with one size of score written on it. You could sort these slips into equal groups with ease, although there might be some left over. And you want *about* 15 equal groups. So you can sort the 46 slips or the 46 possible sizes of score into 15 equal groups. (One slip or one size of score will be left over—you will learn what to do with it.) With $R = 46$ divided into 15 groups (plus one score size left over), what is the number of score sizes in each group—that is, what is i?

Now return to section 60 and choose the right answer for $i = — ? —.$

69   You would make another group with the "extra" score size. Of course! Then you would have 16 groups, comfortably between 10 and 20.

Remember that you have 46 *possible* sizes of score, including the highest and the lowest. You can have a group which includes *sizes* that are not represented in the list of actual scores. For example, the scores on a test might be 50, 48, 45, and so on down to the lowest score; the *possible* sizes are 50, 49, 48, 47, and on down.

In the lowest group you can include possible sizes which are lower than the lowest actual score. And in the highest group you can have possible score sizes which are higher than the highest actual score.

Try another example: If $R = 82$, then $i = $ — ? —.

If you say 5, see section 63.

If you say 6, see section 65.

If you say 8, see section 74.

If you "can't decide," see section 82.

70   With 2 sizes in each group, and a high score of 65, the upper-most group could be 64 and 65 (or 64-65) as usually written. Correct.

But a top group of 65-66 is also correct!
To see why, turn to section 76.

71   You would place 3 score sizes in a group.
This number appears to be just right.

With a range of 39, you could have 13 groups of 3 possible sizes each. (With 4 sizes in a group, you would have only 10 score groups; with 2 sizes, you would have 20 score groups.)

Now, referring to the list of scores in section 75, which score sizes will you place in the top group? They are printed again here.

69	59	55	53	52	50	49	45	43	40
64	58	55	53	52	50	48	45	43	40
63	58	55	53	52	50	47	45	42	37
63	57	54	53	52	49	47	45	42	37
63	57	54	53	52	49	47	45	42	36
62	57	54	53	52	49	47	45	42	35
61	57	54	52	52	49	47	45	42	33
61	56	54	52	51	49	46	44	41	32
61	56	53	52	51	49	46	43	41	31
60	55	53	52	51	49	46	43	40	31

If you think 69-70-71, see section 72.
If you think 68-69-70, see section 87.
If you think 67-68-69, see section 84.
If you think it doesn't make any difference, see section 79.

72   You would place score sizes of 69-70-71 in the top group. Why?

Return to section 76 and reread the rules.

73   With 2 score sizes in each group and a high score of 65, the uppermost group could be 65 and 66 (or 65-66, as usually written). Correct.

But a top group of 64-65 is also correct!

To see why, turn to section 76.

74   With 82 possible sizes of score, you suggest placing 8 sizes in each group. This doesn't square with the rule for grouping scores.

Return to section 60 and retrace your steps.

75 Here are the scores made by 100 students on a test.
(*N* = 100)

69	59	55	53	52	50	49	45	43	40
64	58	55	53	52	50	48	45	43	40
63	58	55	53	52	50	47	45	42	37
63	57	54	53	52	49	47	45	42	37
63	57	54	53	52	49	47	45	42	36
62	57	54	53	52	49	47	45	42	35
61	57	54	52	52	49	47	45	42	33
61	56	54	52	51	49	46	44	41	32
61	56	53	52	51	49	46	43	41	31
60	55	53	52	51	49	46	43	40	31

How many sizes of score should be placed in each group?
(*i* = — ? —)

If you say 2, see section 78.
If you say 3, see section 71.
If you say 4, see section 80.
If you say 7, see section 77.

76   With 2 sizes in each group and a high score of 65, the upper-most group could contain sizes of 64 and 65 *or* of 65 and 66. How can both be feasible?

Because each group must contain 2 *possible* sizes: $i = 2$.

The list of scores might read: 65, 62, 61, 59, etc.

We must have groups which contain the *possible* sizes of 64, 63, and 60, even though we have no *actual* scores of these sizes, in order to have the measures we compute be good approximations of the statistics we are interested in.

We may also have possible score sizes above the highest actual score and below the lowest actual score.

All possible score sizes must be represented in the grouping and the highest score must be included in the uppermost group.

The highest score may be any one of the possible sizes in its group.

If you wish to review the entire process of grouping scores, return to section 55.

If you are ready to group a set of scores, proceed to section 75.

77   You would place 7 sizes of score in a group? No.

You must have divided the *number* of scores by 15.

It would be best for you to return to section 60 and review the grouping procedure.

78   You would place 2 score sizes in a group.

This will give you more groups than you need. $R = 39$; $39 \div 2 =$ about 20; you will have 20 groups.

It will pay you to check in this manner before choosing your group sizes.

You can come closer to the ideal of 15 groups if you return to section 75 and try again.

79   You say it doesn't make any difference which scores are in the top group (as long as this group contains the highest score).

You are correct.

Different groupings will, however, give slightly different values for the averages and the other statistics. It is desirable, therefore, for all students in a class to group scores the same way.

For this reason *only,* we arbitrarily select 67-69 (score sizes of 67, 68, and 69) as the highest group in this practice exercise.

Now, group the 100 scores on your paper, using 67-69 as the highest group, 64-66 as the next, and so on.

To check on your accuracy, if you find the lowest group is:

> 31-33, see section 83.
> 30-32, see section 81.
> 29-31, see section 85.
> 28-30, see section 86.

80   You would place 4 score sizes in a group.

This plan is risky.

Check it out: $R = 39$; $39 \div 4 =$ about 10; you will have 10 groups. Since 10 is the bare minimum, it is best to try to approach more closely the ideal of 15 groups.

Return to section 75 and try again.

81   You have the sizes 30-32 in your lowest group, but you have made an error.

Do you have exactly 3 sizes in every group?

Have you included all of the possible sizes?

Check your work and choose the right answer in section 79.

82   If you cannot quickly decide how many sizes of score to place in each group, you'd better review the grouping procedure, beginning with section 60.

83   Correct, of course. You now have grouped the possible sizes of score, including the largest and the smallest actual scores.

The next step is to determine the number of actual scores in each group of possible sizes.

Referring to the list of 100 scores in section 75, how many scores are in the uppermost group? One, of course.

The number of scores in a group (actual scores, not the possible score sizes) is called the *frequency* of scores, and its symbol is f.

Make a column of frequencies by finding the number of actual scores in each group. Label this column of numbers the f column (f for frequency).

Now, find the sum of the frequencies. The sum should be 100, because you have 100 scores. That is, $\Sigma f = N = 100$.

This list of score groups and frequencies is called a frequency distribution.

Now you will use your frequency distribution. Proceed to section 88.

84   You would place score sizes of 67-68-69 in the top group. Why?

Return to section 76 and reread the rules.

85 You have the sizes 29-31 in your lowest group—but you have made an error.

Do you have exactly 3 sizes in each group?

Have you included all of the possible sizes?

Check your work and choose the right answer in section 79.

86 You have the sizes 28-30 in your lowest group, but the list of scores contains none of these sizes.

Your lowest group must contain the smallest actual score.

Correct your error and choose the right answer in section 79.

87 You would place score sizes of 68-69-70 in the top group. Why?

Return to section 76 and reread the rules.

Computing the Median from a Frequency Distribution

88 The frequency distribution of the 100 scores from section 79 should now look like this:

Scores	f
67-69	1
64-66	1
61-63	7
58-60	4
55-57	10
52-54	24
49-51	14
46-48	9
43-45	12
40-42	10
37-39	2
34-36	2
31-33	4

$$N = 100$$

You can no longer use the methods for computing statistics that you used with small sets of scores—because in the frequency distribution you have in a sense lost the individual scores. For example, you cannot know from the frequency distribution whether the highest score is 67 or 68 or 69.

Hence you now compute statistics by another method which yields estimates, or approximations, of the *median,* the *quartile deviation,* the *mean,* and the *standard deviation.*

Recall that you found the *median* (or mid-point) by counting up half-way in a list of scores which were arrayed in order of size. You were working in line with a definition of the median as "the score-point which separates the top half of the scores

88 from the bottom half." Thus the median does not necessarily
have to be a whole-number score value.

To find the median for grouped scores, you can count the
scores (by adding together the score frequencies) up from the
bottom until you find the group within which the median score-
point lies. Your problem then becomes to estimate the exact
position of the median within this group of scores.

Will the median of a large set of scores determined from a
grouped frequency distribution be the same as the median of
those scores determined by the method used for small sets of
scores?

If you say yes, see section 90.

If you say no, see section 94.

89 Copy the frequency table and compute the median by following these steps:

Scores	f
67-69	1
64-66	1
61-63	7
58-60	4
55-57	10
52-54	24
49-51	14
46-48	9
43-45	12
40-42	10
37-39	2
34-36	2
31-33	4

$$N = 100$$

$$\frac{N}{2} = \text{---} ? \text{---}$$

Counting scores (by adding score frequencies) up from the bottom:

     the subtotal is — ? —
     additional scores needed = — ? —
     correction $= i \times$ fraction $=$ — ? —
     dividing line between groups $=$ — ? —

     median = dividing line + correction
     Md =   — ? — + — ? —

Check your results with section 91.

69

90   You say that the values of the median of a set of scores determined by the two different methods will be the same. But it will almost certainly *not* be the same.

Return to section 88, find the reason why you missed, and choose the correct answer.

91   In computing the median of 100 scores in section 89, you should have found $Md = 50.9$. (One decimal place is sufficient.)

If you do *not* have this answer, turn to section 93 to check your figures.

If you have the correct value, proceed to section 95.

92   You seek an estimate of Md, the median, or the mid-score of the set of scores.

You had 30 scores, and counted up to (but not more than) 15, which is $N/2$.

You counted 14 scores (by adding together the score frequencies) up to the dividing line, which was 32.5 (half-way between the two groups 31-32 and 33-34).

You needed *one more* of the next 4 scores, and these 4 are of the sizes 33 and 34 (because $i = 2$).

Visualize the situation as the diagram shows it on the facing page.

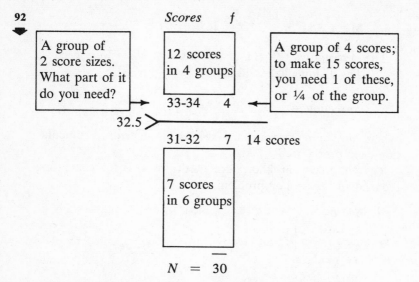

Scores *f*

A group of 2 score sizes. What part of it do you need?

12 scores in 4 groups

33-34   4

A group of 4 scores; to make 15 scores, you need 1 of these, or ¼ of the group.

32.5

31-32   7   14 scores

7 scores in 6 groups

$N = 30$

Just as you need ¼ of the *scores,* you likewise need ¼ of the *sizes* in the group. In other words, you need to go ¼ of the way into the next group of 2 score sizes. Compute:

¼ × 2 = ½ or .5

(In general language, you have multiplied *i* by the fraction.) This product .5 is the "correction" to be added to the dividing line:

32.5 + .5 = 33.0

You have now found the median, *Md:*

$Md = 33.0$

This median is a measure of central tendency, the mid-point of a set of scores.

Proceed now to section 89 and find the median, *Md,* of the 100 scores in the frequency distribution.

$$Md = 48.5 + \frac{11}{14} \times 3 = 48.5 + 2.4 = 50.9$$

The subtotal was 39; 11 of the next 14 scores were needed; $i = 3$. The dividing line is 48.5.

$$\text{correction} = \frac{11}{14} \times 3 = \frac{33}{14} = 2\frac{5}{14} = 2.4$$

Where did you make your mistake? Was it an error in computation or in procedure?

To reinforce your knowledge of the process for computing the median, try another problem.

Scores	f
45-46	1
43-44	1
41-42	2
39-40	5
37-38	6
35-36	3
33-34	2
31-32	4
29-30	3
27-28	3
25-26	3
23-24	2
21-22	2

$$N = 37$$

Copy the frequency table and follow the steps:

$$\frac{N}{2} = - \; ? \; -$$

93 Counting scores up from the bottom,

the subtotal $= - ? -$

additional scores needed to equal $\dfrac{N}{2} = - ? -$

f in the next higher group $= - ? -$
f becomes a fraction $= - ? -$
correction $= i \times$ the fraction
$\qquad = - ? - \times - ? -$
$\qquad = - ? -$
dividing line between groups $= - ? -$

$Md = $ dividing line $+$ correction
$\qquad = - ? - + - ? -$
$\qquad = - ? -$

Check your results in section 96.

94   You say that the values of the median of a set of scores determined by the two different methods will not be the same.

This answer is almost certainly correct, since the value determined from the grouped frequency distribution is only an estimate of the value determined from the exact scores.

To compute a median, use this frequency distribution of 30 scores.

Scores	f
41-42	1
39-40	4
37-38	4
35-36	3
33-34	4

32.5 >————————————

Scores	f	
31-32	7	14 scores
29-30	1	
27-28	2	
25-26	1	
23-24	2	
21-22	0	
19-20	1	

$$N \;=\; 30$$

Count up half-way: to, but not beyond 15:

$$N = 30; \qquad \frac{N}{2} = 15$$

$$1 + 0 + 2 + 1 + 2 + 1 + 7 = 14$$

Draw a line and write the subtotal (14) as in the example.

Md, therefore, will be somewhere in the next higher group (33-34).

The subtotal 14 includes all scores in the group 31-32 and in all groups below.

The "dividing line" between group 31-32 and the next higher

94 group is half-way between the two groups, or at 32.5. *Md* is ⬅ *above* the point 32.5. How far above?

You have 14 scores below the dividing line (obtained by adding together the score frequencies); the subtotal has been marked. But 14 is not enough; you need 15. However, including the next 4 scores (in the next higher group) would make too many. You need *one more* of the next 4 scores, or ¼ of the next group of scores (of which there are 2 sizes; $i = 2$). That is, you need ¼ of 2, or ½, which is .5. The median is located at this distance above the dividing line.

In this example, therefore:

$$Md = 32.5 + .5 = 33.0$$

Do you follow the procedure? If you are not clear, return to the beginning of this section and follow through once more.

If you still do not understand, turn to section 92.

If you feel you can now find the median of the original set of 100 scores from the frequency distribution, proceed to section 89.

95 You have now found an estimate of the median, a measure of central tendency which is the mid-point of a set of scores. (Associate "median" with "middle.") You found the median by what was essentially a counting process.

While this "counting" process is fresh in mind, proceed to section 98.

96   Of the 37 scores in section 93,

$$Md = 34.0$$

If you do *not* have this median, turn to section 97 to find your error.

If you found $Md = 34.0$, return to section 89 and rework Md for the set of 100 scores.

97   In computing the median of 37 scores in section 93, you should have:

$$Md = 32.5 + \frac{1.5}{2} \times 2 = 32.5 + 1.5 = 34.0$$

Where is your error this time? In computation or in procedure?

Return to section 93, correct your error, and proceed as directed.

Computing Quartiles, Deciles, and Percentiles from a Frequency Distribution

98   You have been using a "counting" process to determine the median (a measure of central tendency which is the mid-*point* of a set of scores.)

The same procedure is used to determine the *"quartiles"*— the *points* which separate the distribution of scores into fourths. (The middle quartile, Q_2, is the same score-point as the median, since it separates the upper half of the scores from the lower half.)

This process can also be used to find the score-points (called *"deciles"*) which divide the set of scores into tenths and the score-points (called *"percentiles"*) which divide the set of scores into hundredths. But first let us consider the quartiles. [Turn the page.]

98 Using the same 100 scores as before (from section 75) in the
same frequency distribution (see below), locate the first quartile,
Q_1, the point which separates the lowest fourth of the scores
from the rest of the scores.

Scores	f
67-69	1
64-66	1
61-63	7
58-60	4
55-57	10
52-54	24
49-51	14
46-48	9
43-45	12
40-42	10
37-39	2
34-36	2
31-33	4

$$N = 100$$

98 Write out the problem, using this form:

$$\frac{N}{4} = -\,?\,-.$$

Counting scores upward,

the subtotal $= -\,?\,-$

additional scores needed to equal $\dfrac{N}{4} = -\,?\,-$

f in the next higher group $= -\,?\,-$

f becomes a fraction $= -\,?\,-$

correction $= i \times$ the fraction $= -\,?\,-$

dividing line between groups $= -\,?\,-$

dividing line $+$ correction $= Q_1 = -\,?\,- + -\,?\,-$

$\qquad\qquad\qquad\qquad\quad = -\,?\,-$

If your answer is 44.2, 44.25, or 44.3, go to section 101.

If you have arrived at any other answer, go to section 102.

99   After having computed the median (*Md*), the first quartile (Q_1), and the third quartile (Q_3), you will find it easy to compute deciles and percentiles.

We can divide a set of scores into tenths by computing the nine score-points called *deciles*. We already have computed the middle one, D_5; it is the median.

Just as the deciles are score-points which divide test scores into tenths, the *percentiles* are the 99 score-points which divide a distribution of test scores into hundredths. Thus the first decile, D_1, is the same as the tenth percentile, P_{10}, just as a dime is the same as ten cents. And $P_{50} = D_5 = Md$.

You have already computed Q_1 and Q_3. What percentiles are they? [To check your answer, see the last page of this section.]

➡

Scores	f
67-69	1
64-66	1
61-63	7
58-60	4
55-57	10
52-54	24
49-51	14
46-48	9
43-45	12
40-42	10
37-39	2
34-36	2
31-33	4

$$N = 100$$

To compute P_{10}, count up one-tenth (10%) of the scores and follow the same procedure used in computing Md.

Compute P_{10} and P_{90} for the set of scores summarized by the frequency table above. Your answers should be:

$$P_{10} = 40.1 \qquad \text{and} \qquad P_{90} = 59.8$$

Percentiles usually need not be computed by teachers because there are better ways of interpreting the test results of a single class or of several classes. We must understand the meaning, however, because the results of "standardized" or published tests used in high school or in college are often reported in a table of percentile ranks. Technically, *percentile ranks* are different from percentiles. For all practical purposes, however, the differences are so slight that we may interpret percentile ranks as though they are in fact percentiles. But percentile ranks have serious limitations in test interpretation and you should be aware of these if you may be expected to deal with percentile ranks.

Percentiles are unequal measurement units which cannot be

99 combined or averaged (hence are sometimes called "dead end" ➤ scores). The reason is that scores tend to bunch up near the middle of a distribution; percentiles are based on the number of scores rather than the sizes of scores, so they also tend to pile up near the middle. As a result, P_{40} may appear to be much further below P_{50} than it really is because the scores at these points are nearly the same. The difference between P_{10} and P_{20} may represent a far greater difference in score value.

The only use of percentiles or percentile ranks is to indicate a student's standing in a group of others.

You were asked on page 82 what percentiles are equivalent to Q_1 and Q_3. If your answers were, respectively, P_{25} and P_{75}, you are right. If you are wrong, rethink the question and review the explanations. If you found the right answers for P_{10} and P_{90} of the frequency distribution in this section, good. If you didn't, review the process of computing Q_1 and Q_3 in sections 98 and 101 and apply the thinking to the process of computing percentiles. If you do not understand the processes and the explanations, get help. (A few helpful books are listed on page 175; if you are enrolled in a class which is studying statistics, ask your instructor for help).

When you do understand this section, go on to section 103.

100   Your answer is wrong. Check your work against these operations:

$$\frac{3}{4}N = 75$$

subtotal = 53
additional scores needed = 22 of the next 24

$$\text{correction} = 3 \times \frac{22}{24} = \frac{66}{24} = 2\frac{18}{24} = 2.75$$

$$Q_3 = 51.5 + 2.75$$
$$= 54.25 \text{ (or 54.2 or 54.3)}$$

Compare this computation with your work in section 101. If you see your mistake and feel sure you would not make the same error in another computation, follow the directions given at the end of section 101 for the answer you have reached.

101 Any of the three answers is correct, if you reached them by computing correctly. The process of computation in section 98 should have yielded 44.25 as the value of Q_1. This may be rounded off to one decimal place, indicating that Q_1 is "between 44 and 45." We need to locate the point which separates the lowest fourth of the scores from the three other fourths, and that point is all we need to locate. It is not necessarily a whole-number point, and need not be computed beyond the first decimal. Accordingly, Q_1 computed as 44.25 may be rounded off, as was said before.

When it is necessary to round off a number that ends with exactly 5, it is *usually* better to round it off to the nearest even value; by this rule, 44.25 would be rounded down to 44.2. However, in computing quartiles, deciles, and percentiles, it is better to round all such numbers up to the next higher value; therefore, in the example of section 98, 44.25 would be rounded up to 44.3.

Now that you have computed correctly the first quartile, Q_1, you are ready to compute the third quartile, Q_3, of the same set of scores.

Scores	f
67-69	1
64-66	1
61-63	7
58-60	4
55-57	10
52-54	24
49-51	14
46-48	9
43-45	12
40-42	10
37-39	2
34-36	2
31-33	4

$$N = 100$$

▼

101 The third quartile, Q_3, is the point which separates the highest fourth of the scores from the three other fourths. You are to compute Q_3, using the frequency table printed here.

This quartile can be computed by counting down one-fourth of the scores from the top, or by counting up three-fourths of the scores from the bottom. If you prefer to follow a familiar pattern, then, count up from the bottom as you have been doing. If you count down, remember to subtract instead of add! Do you see why?

Show all the steps, following the usual pattern:

$$\frac{3}{4}N = \text{— ? —} \qquad \text{or} \qquad \frac{3N}{4} = \text{— ? —}$$

Counting scores up,

subtotal $= \text{— ? —}$

additional scores needed to equal $\dfrac{3N}{4} = \text{— ? —}$

f in the next higher group $= \text{— ? —}$
f becomes a fraction $= \text{— ? —}$
correction $= i \times$ the fraction $= \text{— ? —}$
dividing line between groups $= \text{— ? —}$
dividing line $+$ correction $= Q_3 = \text{— ? —} + \text{— ? —}$
$\qquad\qquad\qquad\qquad\qquad = \text{— ? —}$

If you have arrived at 54.2, 54.25, or 54.3 as your answer, go to section 99.

If you have arrived at any other answer, go to section 100.

102 Your answer in section 98 was wrong. Examine the computation by which the correct answer is found:

$$\frac{N}{4} = \frac{100}{4} = 25$$

The subtotal is 18; 7 additional scores of the next 12 are needed.

The fraction is $\frac{7}{12}$ and is multiplied by 3:

$$3 \times \frac{7}{12} = \frac{21}{12} = 1\frac{9}{12} = 1.75$$

The dividing line between groups 40-42 and 43-45 is at 42.5.

$Q_1 = 42.5 + 1.75 = 44.25$, which is rounded up to 44:3

Now compare this computation with the one you made using the outline in section 98. If you perceive your error and are confident that you will not make the same mistake again, follow the directions given at the end of section 98 for the answer you have reached.

Simple Measures of Dispersion in Large Sets of Scores

103   Using a set of 100 test scores distributed in a frequency distribution, you have computed the location of a measure of central tendency, the median. You have also computed the location of the analogous measures called the quartiles, the deciles, and the percentiles. You are now ready to compute some related measures of dispersion.

You have located the points Q_1 and Q_3 and will use them to compute Q, the *quartile deviation*.

The quartile deviation is defined as "half the difference between the third quartile and the first quartile," or

$$Q = \frac{Q_3 - Q_1}{2}$$

Why "half the difference"? No really important reason.

Q is sometimes called the "semi-interquartile range," but "quartile deviation" is a simpler term.

You found $Q_1 = 44.3$ in section 98 and $Q_3 = 54.3$ in section 101.

$$Q = - ? -$$

Check your answer in section 106.

104   This answer is wrong. Did you forget the definition of range? Return to section 109 and try again.

105   This answer required ingenuity, but it is wrong. Do you remember the definition of range?

Return to section 109 and look again!

106 $Q = 5.0$

If you do not have this exact answer, return to section 103 and check your work.

If you found $Q = 5.0$, proceed to section 109.

107   You are right; of course you can't find the range in a grouped frequency distribution. The individual scores are lost in such a distribution and it is impossible to determine the highest and the lowest scores.

Range is *not* one of the measures of dispersion which can be determined from grouped data.

You have now computed the median and the quartile deviation of a set of 100 test scores. Thus you have a measure of central tendency and a measure of dispersion. You can *summarize* the 100 scores by reporting this pair of measures.

If you wish to stop and review at this point, you may return to the computation of the median, which began with section 88.

A set of scores may also be summarized by reporting another pair of measures, the mean (*Mn*) and the *standard deviation* (σ). These measures are more useful than the others, so proceed to compute the mean in section 113.

108   How did you get this answer?

Did you subtract the lower frequency of the lowest class from the higher frequency of the highest class? Your method was wrong—how could you know that any score is 31 or 69? Go back to section 109, and try again.

But maybe you followed another method, going back to section 75, and thus you know that the lowest score is 31 and the highest score 69 because you looked at the original set of scores. If this was your method, you violated instructions and have not learned something that you should understand before you go ahead. You were asked, "Can you determine the range of scores *from this distribution?*" Return to section 109, and answer the question if you can.

109   You have found from a frequency distribution one measure of the dispersion of a set of 100 scores, namely the quartile deviation, Q. Now proceed to another, using the same frequency table from which you computed the quartiles, and from them in turn Q. This frequency distribution is printed here to save you looking back to section 98 for it.

Scores	f
67-69	1
64-66	1
61-63	7
58-60	4
55-57	10
52-54	24
49-51	14
46-48	9
43-45	12
40-42	10
37-39	2
34-36	2
31-33	4

$$N = 100$$

Can you determine the range of the scores from this distribution?

$$R = — ? —$$

If you have 38 for your answer, proceed to section 108.
If you have 36, go to section 105.
If you have 34, go to section 104.
If you cannot determine the range of the scores, go to section 107.

Computing the Mean from a Frequency Distribution

110 $\qquad$ correction $= 3 \times \dfrac{-10}{100} = -.3$

$Mn = 50.0 - .3 = 49.7$

This figure is the mean of the 100 test scores in the frequency distribution. If you have a different value, proceed to section 111 to investigate your error.

If you have computed the correct answer ($Mn = 49.7$), you have a choice:

Either: You may review the computation of the mean by turning to section 116 and working another problem.

Or: You may proceed immediately to the next statistic in section 120.

Check your figures with these:

$$Mn = 50.0 - 3 \times \frac{-10}{100}$$

$$= 50.0 - .3$$

$$= 49.7$$

The assumed mean is 50.0 (the mid-point of the score group 49-51).

$\Sigma fd = -10$ (that is, the total of $+95$ and -105)

$$\frac{\Sigma fd}{N} \times i = -\frac{10}{100} \times 3 = -.3$$

$$Mn = 50.0 - .3 = 49.7$$

Where did you make your error? Was it in understanding or in computation?

Try another example, using this frequency distribution:

Scores	f
45-46	1
43-44	1
41-42	2
39-40	5
37-38	6
35-36	3
33-34	2
31-32	4
29-30	3
27-28	3
25-26	3
23-24	2
21-22	2
	—
N = 37	

◄

111 Complete the frequency table, adding d and fd columns;
assume a mean in any group.

Assumed mean is — ? —

$$\Sigma fd = \text{— ? —}$$

Is the — ? — plus or minus?

$$\frac{\Sigma fd}{N} \times i = \text{— ? —}$$

Is the — ? — plus or minus?

$$Mn = \underline{\hspace{2cm}} + \underline{\hspace{2cm}} = \text{— ? —}$$

Check your answer in section 119.

112 Correct. The assumed mean is 50.0, the mid-point of the group 49-51.

This assumed mean is almost certain to be too low or too high. You need to compute a correction for it. You begin the computation of this correction by determining how much each *group* of scores deviates from the assumed mean.

The group 49-51 has a deviation of 0, that is, no deviation or zero deviation.

The group 52-54 is one step above the zero-deviation group; it has a deviation of $+1$ (that is, plus 1; it is customary to omit writing the plus sign because numbers are considered plus or positive unless otherwise labeled).

The group 46-48 has a deviation of -1 (that is, minus 1; the minus sign is to be written).

Write all of the deviations in a column next to the frequencies. Label this column d.

Next, multiply each frequency by its corresponding deviation, making another column. Label this column fd (meaning $f \times d$).

◄►

Scores	f	d	fd
67-69	1	—	—
64-66	1	—	—
61-63	7	—	—
58-60	4	—	—
55-57	10	—	—
52-54	24	1	—
49-51	14	0	—
46-48	9	− 1	—
43-45	12	—	—
40-42	10	—	—
37-39	2	—	—
34-36	2	—	—
31-33	4	—	—

$$N = 100$$

Note that deviations above the 0 (zero) deviation are + (plus or positive) deviations. Deviations below the 0 are − (minus or negative deviations).

What is your d for the score group 67-69? What is your fd for the score group 31-33? If the former is 6 and the latter is −24 (minus 24), you are probably on the right track and you should check your complete table with section 117. If you have any other values, try to find your mistake before you go to section 117.

113   In section 88 you set up a frequency distribution of 100
scores. It is printed again here.

Scores	f
67-69	1
64-66	1
61-63	7
58-60	4
55-57	10
52-54	24
49-51	14
46-48	9
43-45	12
40-42	10
37-39	2
34-36	2
31-33	4

$$N = 100$$

You are now to find the mean of these 100 scores, using this
frequency distribution; you cannot compute the mean directly
from the scores themselves because you do not have them—the
individual scores have become lost in the frequency distribution.
It will be necessary to estimate the mean, using a computing procedure.

To start, you guess a mean; in careful language, you select
an *assumed mean.* This will be either too high or too low. Then
you compute a *correction,* to lower or raise the assumed mean.
The closer your guess is to the assumed mean, the smaller will
be the correction. But no matter where in the frequency distribution you guess the mean to be (subject to one restriction),
the correction will result in the best estimate of the mean and
the same value for the estimate.

The one restriction on your guessing is this: the assumed
mean must be the mid-point of a score group. You can place
your guess in any score group, but you may save some work

113 if you succeed in guessing the score group in which the mean lies, or a score group close to it.

Suppose you guess the mean to be in the middle group (the 7th of the 13 groups). The middle group contains 14 scores of sizes 49, 50, and 51. What will be the assumed mean?

If you say 50.0, see section 112.

If you say some other number, turn to section 115.

114   From the frequency table in section 117, you should have obtained the following data:

The sum of the positive *fd's* is 95 (that is, $+95$).

The sum of the negative *fd's* is -105 (minus 105).

The total of the sums is -10; that is, $\Sigma fd = -10$.

The correction will be a minus (negative) number, lowering the assumed mean.

Unless you have these answers you have made some error of computing or understanding. Either kind of error will prevent your succeeding with the work that is to come. If your answer is wrong as to the sums of the positive or negative *fd's*, you need to go back to section 117 or to section 112 and restudy your work until you get the right answers and know why. But if you have these two sums right but have their total wrong, here are a few hints:

The total of $+6$ and -5 is $+1$.

The total of -6 and $+5$ is -1.

Now, what is the total of $+95$ and -105? In other words, what is Σfd?

If these hints do not enable you to understand, you need help from a teacher and should seek it.

If you have the right answers, proceed now to finish computing the correction.

The total, Σfd, is the basis of the correction. It is not yet the correction. It must have two modifications:

First: The f in Σfd is for N scores, in the present problem 100 scores. To get an f that is the mean of all these f's, you must divide the f by N, in the present problem by 100.

Second: The d in Σfd is for groups of score sizes, not for single score sizes. To get a d that applies to single score sizes, you must multiply the d of Σfd by i, the number of score sizes in a group, in the present problem by 3.

In making these modifications you need not separate the f

§ **114**   100

114 and *d* out of Σ*fd;* instead, you simply divide Σ*fd* by *N* and multiply it by *i*. This process gives you the correction:

$$\text{correction} = i \times \frac{\Sigma fd}{N} = -?-$$

In the problem you are solving, the — ? — is a minus (negative) number, as you decided earlier in this section. Compute this correction.

Now you get the mean by adding this correction to the assumed mean. In this addition operation, remember that (in the present problem) one of the numbers is a minus number. You can fill in these blanks below:

$$Mn = AMn + \text{correction} = -?-$$

or

$$Mn = \underline{\hspace{1cm}} + \underline{\hspace{1cm}} = -?-$$

If you prefer formulas, the complete formula is

$$Mn = AMn + \left(i \times \frac{\Sigma fd}{N} \right)$$

Formulas are easily forgotten, so concentrate on the steps in the process.

Check your results in section 110.

115   Look again. The assumed mean is the mid-point of the score group 49-51, which contains the score sizes 49, 50, and 51. Return to section 113 and correct your answer.

You have computed the mean of the 100 scores, beginning with an assumed mean at the mid-point of the middle group of scores, the group 49-51. You have arrived at $Mn = 49.7$.

Compute the mean once more, with an assumed mean in any other group you may choose. If you choose the lowest group, 31-33, you may have an especially interesting experience.

Scores	f
67-69	1
64-66	1
61-63	7
58-60	4
55-57	10
52-54	24
49-51	14
46-48	9
43-45	12
40-42	10
37-39	2
34-36	2
31-33	4

$$N = 100$$

Write the problem in this form:

$$AMn = -\,?\,-$$

$$\Sigma fd = -\,?\,-$$

$$\frac{\Sigma fd}{N} = -\,?\,-$$

$$i = -\,?\,-$$

$$i \times \frac{\Sigma fd}{N} = -\,?\,-$$

$$Mn = -\,?\,- + -\,?\,- = -\,?\,-$$

Check your result in section 118.

103

117　The frequency table you prepared in section 112 should look
like this one. If it does not, return to section 112 and compute
and think until you have these values and know why you have
them; then come back here.

Scores	f	d	fd
67-69	1	6	6
64-66	1	5	5
61-63	7	4	28
58-60	4	3	12
55-57	10	2	20
52-54	24	1	24
49-51	14	0	0
46-48	9	−1	− 9
43-45	12	−2	− 24
40-42	10	−3	− 30
37-39	2	−4	− 8
34-36	2	−5	− 10
31-33	4	−6	− 24
	100		

The assumed mean is 50.0, the mid-point of the group 49-51,
which has zero deviation. This assumed mean is to be corrected;
the amount of the correction will be computed by operations
now to be explained and performed.

Each frequency f has been multiplied by its deviation d to
produce the fd column. The fd's indicate the importance of the
scores, their pull. The 10 scores in the group 40-42 are more
important in pulling the assumed mean than the 10 scores in the
group 55-57, for the d of the one *is* −3 and its fd is −30
whereas the d of the other is 2 and its fd is 20 (which means
−30 pulling down and +20 pulling up).

Now, add the positive fd's (those above 0). What is the sum?
Next, add the negative fd's (those below 0). What is the sum?
Now add the two sums. What is their total?
This total is an *algebraic* sum, and therefore it may be a plus

117 or positive number or it may be a minus or negative number. It is represented by the symbol Σfd, that is, the sum of the fd's. You therefore need to answer the question

$$\Sigma fd = \text{—}\ ?\ \text{—}$$

and if the — ? — is a minus number you write the minus sign.

This sum Σfd is not the correction but it tells you some things about the correction:

If Σfd is a plus number, the assumed mean is too low, the correction will be a plus (positive) number, and it will raise the assumed mean.

If Σfd is a minus number, the assumed mean is too high, the correction will be a minus (negative) number, and it will lower the assumed mean.

Will the correction be a plus number and raise the assumed mean, or a minus number and lower it?

You have been asked several questions in this section. If you have answered them correctly, you are ready to continue computing the correction for the assumed mean. Go ahead to section 114 to check your answers.

118   The mean of the 100 scores should be the same, 49.7, no matter which group you selected to include the assumed mean.

If you obtained this exact value, proceed to section 120.

If you have a different value for the mean, return to section 116 and check each value. Double-check your arithmetic. You must obtain the correct value of Mn before proceeding.

119   You should have found the mean of the 37 scores to be 33.3. Since you could have assumed a mean in any of the groups, we cannot check your figures for each value of f and d.

If you do not have $Mn = 33.3$, return to section 111 and check your work. You must find your error and correct it before you can proceed. If you feel your difficulty is with the plus and minus numbers, you might try putting the assumed mean in the lowest group of score sizes; if then you do your work correctly you will get the correct value for the correction and the mean.

If you have the correct value of Mn, return to section 113 and again compute the mean for the original 100 scores.

Computing the Standard Deviation
from a Frequency Distribution

120   You have computed the mean of a set of scores in two operations:

(1) You prepared a frequency table with columns f, d and fd.

(2) You guessed the mean and corrected your guess.

Remember that the mean is a measure of central tendency which is affected by the size of every score when it is computed directly from ungrouped scores. When the scores have been grouped the estimated value of the mean is affected by the approximate value of every score. (Why "approximate"?)

The measure of dispersion related to the mean is the standard deviation. Its symbol is σ, the lower-case Greek letter sigma. It was defined and explained in section 43, and then computed for a small set of scores. Now you are to compute it for a large set of scores, making such changes and adjustments as are necessitated by the grouping of the scores.

To compute σ, use the same frequency distribution of 100 scores with its f, d, and fd columns. It is printed again here. The middle group, 49-51, was selected to be the 0 deviation group.

◄

Scores	f	d	fd
67-69	1	6	6
64-66	1	5	5
61-63	7	4	28
58-60	4	3	12
55-57	10	2	20
52-54	24	1	24
49-51	14	0	0
46-48	9	-1	-9
43-45	12	-2	-24
40-42	10	-3	-30
37-39	2	-4	-8
34-36	2	-5	-10
31-33	4	-6	-24
	100		

The next step is to make another column by multiplying each fd by its corresponding d. Label this column fd^2 (which is equivalent to $fd \times d$).

Now find the sum of the fd^2 column.

$$\Sigma fd^2 = \underline{\quad} ? \underline{\quad}$$

If your sum is -100, turn to section 124.
If your sum is 646, see section 122.

121   Review the computation of σ, the standard deviation, by repeating the process using this distribution of scores:

Scores	f
45-46	1
43-44	1
41-42	2
39-40	5
37-38	6
35-36	3
33-34	2
31-32	4
29-30	3
27-28	3
25-26	3
23-24	2
21-22	2

$$N = 37$$

Complete the frequency table, using the middle group as your zero group; add the columns d, fd, and fd^2. (Remember that $fd^2 = d \times fd$.)

Find Σfd and Σfd^2. (Check your addition.)

$$\frac{\Sigma fd^2}{N} = - \; ? \; -$$

Now, find the correction and square it:

$$c = \frac{\Sigma fd}{N} = - \; ? \; -; \qquad c^2 = - \; ? \; -$$

Subtract (always) c^2:

$$\frac{\Sigma fd^2}{N} - c^2 = - \; ? \; -$$

➤

121 Take the square root:

$$\sqrt{\dfrac{\Sigma fd^2}{N} - c^2} = - \ ? -$$

And don't forget the last step: multiply by i.

$$\sigma = i\sqrt{\dfrac{\Sigma fd^2}{N} - c^2} = - \ ? -$$

Check your result in section 132.

122   Correct. $\Sigma fd^2 = 646$. This is the sum of the squares of the deviations of score groups from the assumed mean.

Next, divide Σfd^2 by N. Since in this example $N = 100$, you need merely to point off two decimal places.

$$\frac{\Sigma fd^2}{N} = \frac{646}{100} = 6.46$$

This division is the first computational step you take after completing the frequency table with its fd^2 column: Divide Σfd^2 by N.

Next comes your second step: You want to convert this figure into one that will apply to the mean rather than to the assumed mean. You begin this conversion in the fd column by getting the fd for the difference between the mean and the assumed mean. This is called c, and is equal to $\dfrac{\Sigma fd}{N}$ * You therefore compute:

$$c = \frac{\Sigma fd}{N} = - \; ? \; -$$

Your second step is not yet completed, however: You still need to square the value of c and subtract c^2 from the mean of the fd^2 column, which you computed in your first step. So you compute:

$$\frac{\Sigma fd^2}{N} - c^2 = - \; ? \; -$$

➡

---

* You may recognize that c is the mean of the fd's, and you will be correct as well as observant. This mean is also, and always, the fd for the difference between the assumed mean and the mean. You can figure out why if you are determined to understand.

122 Note well: The correction factor c is squared and subtracted.*

You have now computed: *first,* the mean of the squares of the deviations of score groups from the assumed mean; *second,* a correction factor; *last,* a corrected value for your first figure so that it is appropriate to the mean rather than the assumed mean. If you do not understand, work through this section again; when you do, check your computations with section 126.

---

* If you are extremely alert, you may ask, "Always subtract? Never add?" Yes. And here is why: You have taken your d from the assumed mean, not from the mean. If you had taken d from the mean, then the assumed mean would deviate from the mean; instead of the assumed mean having 0 in the d and fd and fd^2 columns, it would have numbers and its fd^2 would be a plus number and so would its $\dfrac{\Sigma fd^2}{N}$; you therefore need to subtract something from the value you have computed for $\dfrac{\Sigma fd^2}{N}$ in order to make this value correct for the mean rather than for the assumed mean. It doesn't matter whether the assumed mean is less or more than the mean; you always subtract this correction.

123   **Right.** $c = -\dfrac{10}{100} = -.1;\; c^2 = -.1 \times -.1 = +.01.$

Then $6.46 - .01 = 6.45$ (remembering that c^2 is always subtracted from $\dfrac{\Sigma f d^2}{N}$).

Now you have the "corrected mean of the sum of the squares of the deviations from the assumed mean." This is the meaning of the formula; you have found:

$$\frac{\Sigma f d^2}{N} - c^2.$$

Just two further steps remain: *first,* to extract the square root of 6.45; second, to multiply by i.

Several methods of finding square root were listed in section 49: by computation, by the use of the slide rule or of numerical tables, and by the method of approximation. Any of these methods may be used in computing standard deviation.

Using any method you prefer, find the square root of 6.45.

Check you answer with section 130.

124   To get this sum, you must have ignored one of the mathematical facts of life: "a minus number times a minus number equals a plus number." Therefore, all of the numbers in the fd^2 column are positive.

Return to section 120 and get rid of those minus signs in the fd^2 column; then add the fd^2 column again.

125   You should have these approximate values:

Exercise 1. $Md = 46.5$; $Q_1 = 37$; $Q_3 = 60$; $Q = 11$ or $Q = 12$; $Mn = 47$ or $Mn = 48$; $\sigma = 14$ or $\sigma = 15$.

Exercise 2. $Md = 51.3$ to 52.3; $Q_1 = 44.0$ to 45.5; $Q_3 = 57.5$ to 58.0; $Q = 6$ or $Q = 7$; $Mn = 50.7$ to 51.7; $\sigma = 10.8$ to 11.0.

If you have these answers, you presumably understand the computation of the measures of central tendency and dispersion. Go to section 135 and begin studying measures of statistical relationship. You may want to see the introductory material that precedes section 135.

126   What value do you have for $\dfrac{\Sigma f d^2}{N} - c^2$?

If it is 6.45, see section 123.
If it is 6.36, see section 131.
If it is 6.47, see section 128.

127   You should have 2 score-sizes in a group and find these approximate values: $Md = 34$; $Q_1 = 30$; $Q_3 = 39$; $Q = 4.5$ to 5.0; $Mn = 34.5$; $\sigma = 6.4$ to 6.8.

Now turn to the assignment, section 134.

128 Your answer is wrong. Apparently you added .01 to 6.46. When $-.1$ was multiplied by $-.1$, it became $+.01$. But c^2 is *always* subtracted from $\dfrac{\Sigma fd^2}{N}$

Return to section 122 and correct your error.

129   Given 60 test scores:

Score	f	Score	f	Score	f
48	2	39	1	31	6
46	1	38	3	30	3
45	2	37	2	29	6
44	1	36	5	26	2
43	3	35	2	25	2
42	2	34	3	24	1
41	1	33	4	23	2
40	3	32	2	21	1

Make a frequency table and compute: Md, Q_1, Q_3, Q, Mn, and σ.

(You should be able to complete this entire assignment in less than an hour.)

If you have difficulty with any of the statistics, you can look them up:

> Md, section 88
> Q_1, section 98
> Q_3, section 101
> Q, section 103
> Mn, section 113
> σ, section 120

To check your answers, see the approximate values in section 127.

130   The square root of 6.45 is between 2.5 and 2.6. Approximation methods may give the one or the other. Precise methods give 2.54 when the value of the square root is rounded off to two decimal places. Use the value you found (if it is between 2.5 and 2.6).

The last step in computing σ (the standard deviation) is to multiply by i. (Why? For the same reason that you multiplied by i to get the mean, in section 114.) For this frequency distribution, $i = 3$, and the result is between 7.5 and 7.8.

To summarize the process of finding the standard deviation:

Complete the frequency table with the fd^2 column and add the fd^2's to find Σfd^2.

Divide Σfd^2 by N to obtain $\dfrac{\Sigma fd^2}{N}$.

Subtract c^2 (remembering that $c = \dfrac{\Sigma fd}{N}$).

Extract the square root of $\left(\dfrac{\Sigma fd^2}{N} - c^2\right)$.

Multiply by i.

Thus, $\sigma = i\sqrt{\dfrac{\Sigma fd^2}{N} - c^2}$.

To review the entire process by working another example, turn to section 121.

If you wish to proceed to the next step, consider:

What does σ mean?
What good is it?

Section 133 will tell you.

131   Wrong. Apparently you erred in squaring 0.1.

$$.1 \times .1 = .01 \qquad \text{or} \qquad \frac{1}{10} \times \frac{1}{10} = \frac{1}{100}$$

Return to section 122 and correct your error.

You should have obtained approximately 6.4.

If you have about this value, and if you understand the process, proceed to section 133 to find out what σ means and how it is used.

If you do not have approximately 6.4, re-work the problem, starting with the middle group as the zero group (if you have not already set up this way), and check all of your figures:

Scores	f	d	fd	fd^2
45-46	1	6	6	36
43-44	1	5	5	25
41-42	2	4	8	32
39-40	5	3	15	· 45
37-38	6	2	12	24
35-36	3	1	3	3
33-34	2	0	0	0
31-32	4	−1	− 4	4
29-30	3	−2	− 6	12
27-28	3	−3	− 9	27
25-26	3	−4	− 12	48
23-24	2	−5	− 10	50
21-22	2	−6	− 12	72
	37		+ 49	378
			− 53	

$$\sigma = 2\sqrt{\frac{378}{37} - \left(\frac{-4}{37}\right)^2} = 2\sqrt{10.22 - .01} = 6.4$$

Now, review the process in section 121, or proceed to section 133.

133   The standard deviation is a measure of dispersion. It is one statistic (and a good one) for reporting the variation or spread of a set of scores. To see why it is used, consider the facts in the next paragraph.

Scores	f	d	fd	fd^2
67-69	1	6	6	36
64-66	1	5	5	25
61-63	7	4	28	112
58-60	4	3	12	36
55-57	10	2	20	40
52-54	24	1	24	24
49-51	14	0	0	0
46-48	9	-1	-9	9
43-45	12	-2	-24	48
40-42	10	-3	-30	90
37-39	2	-4	-8	32
34-36	2	-5	-10	50
31-33	4	-6	-24	144
	100		-10	646

$$Md = 50.8; \quad Q = 5.0$$
$$Mn = 49.7; \quad \sigma = 7.6$$

You found the mean of the 100 scores to be 49.7 and the standard deviation to be 7.6 (approximately). Although you cannot say that the average is high or low, or that the spread is large or small, you can use these statistics for comparison. For example, a score may be above or below the mean—but how far? If you say that a score is 57 and that it is 7.6 above the mean of 49.7, you are describing a raw score. But if you say that a score is approximately one sigma (or 1 σ, or one standard deviation) above the mean, you are describing a standard score. A score of 65 is about two sigmas above the mean of the 100 scores (for $49.7 + 15.2 = 64.9$). In this way, raw scores from different tests can be converted into standard scores which can be combined and averaged (as the raw scores cannot—for though you can go through the motions of combining and averaging raw scores from different tests, the results are nonsense).

The mean and the standard deviation can also be used to compare the performance of one class or group of students with that of another. When the class average score on a certain test is the same in two classes, is the performance of the two classes comparable? If the scores are well spread out throughout the range, for one class, and bunched up near the average for the other, the standard deviation in the spread-out set will be larger than the standard deviation in the bunched-up set.

Both dispersion and average (standard deviation and mean) must be considered in comparing sets of scores.

If you wish to review any of the statistical processes of computation for large sets of test scores:

> *Md* begins with section 88.
> *Q* begins with section 98.
> *Mn* begins with section 113.
> σ (standard deviation) begins with section 120.

If you wish another practice run-through of all statistics computed from grouped scores, turn to section 129.

If you are ready for a test of your proficiency, see section 134.

General Assignment

Exercise 1. Given the scores:

80	66	61	58	50	46	43	38	35	29
76	66	60	58	49	46	43	37	35	26
76	64	59	57	49	45	42	37	34	26
72	64	59	55	49	45	42	37	33	26
72	64	59	55	49	44	42	37	33	25
71	62	58	55	48	44	42	36	32	23
70	62	58	51	48	44	40	36	31	21
68	61	58	50	47	44	39	35	29	20

Find: Two measures of central tendency: the mean (Mn) and the median (Md).

Also find: Two measures of dispersion: the quartile deviation (Q) and the standard deviation (σ).

➥

Exercise 2. Given the scores:

76	69	68	68	68	66	66	64	62	61
61	60	59	59	58	57	57	57	57	56
55	55	55	54	53	53	53	52	52	52
52	52	51	50	50	49	49	49	48	47
47	46	45	45	44	44	44	43	42	40
40	39	39	38	37	37	32	28	26	24

Find: The median, *Md;* the quartiles, Q_1 and Q_3; the quartile deviation, *Q.*

Also find: The mean, *Mn;* the standard deviation, σ.

If you wish to check your answers for these two exercises, see section 125. If you do not so wish, go to section 135 and begin learning about statistical measures of relationship. You may want to see the introductory material preceding section 135.

Part Three

MEASURES OF RELATIONSHIP

The statistics computed thus far are used for summarizing or describing a set of scores and to provide one or more bases for interpreting a single score. Occasionally it becomes desirable to compare the measures of one kind of performance with those of another. Examples: How does reading speed compare with reading comprehension? What is the relationship between achievement and ability? How do the scores on a test of statistical computation compare with scores on a test which measures understanding of statistical concepts?

It is easy to compare the measures for a single student when his scores have been interpreted as high or average or low, but how can the performance of an entire class be compared? A single statistic which summarizes the relationship between two sets of test scores may be desired. One of the uses of such a statistic is for prediction. For example, high-school counselors may collect data for several years and then be able to determine which measure or combination of measures is most useful in predicting success in college.

There are several statistics that measure relationship between two sets of scores. The one most frequently used is the *coefficient of correlation*. In Part Three, we present a procedure for computing this measure using individual scores. This method is useful in comparing two sets of scores for a single class. As with other measures, the scores can be grouped and a modified procedure used. This more complex procedure is explained in several books listed among A Few Useful References, page 175.

The Concept of Correlation

135   In many of the common things which you can measure, you notice a relationship. A child 12 years old is larger than one 6 years old; a child of age 6 is larger than one of age 2. As the age of a growing child increases, his size also increases. Of course, not all children of a given age are the same size. And children do not all grow at the same rate. Nevertheless, you can say that there *is* an observable relationship between age (chronological age) and some measure of size, such as height or weight.

Is there is a relationship between the height and the weight of growing boys?

If you answer "yes," see section 143.

If your answer is "no," see section 139.

136   You have said that the correlation between altitude and atmospheric pressure is negative. This answer is correct. As altitude increases, the atmospheric pressure decreases. By definition, there is *negative* correlation whenever the measure of one variable decreases as the measure of the other variable increases.

One further point: the concept of correlation is meaningful only between measures that are in some way *connected*. You cannot, for example, compare food expenditures in Seattle with family incomes in Denver. You need *pairs* of measures (or scores) to measure correlation—and a pair is not just any two; you know that two shoes are not necessarily a pair.

Suppose a teacher has two classes in history; by mid-term, she has given two unit tests. Which of the following comparisons can she make by computing a measure of correlation?

The scores made by the first-period class with the scores of the third-period class on the Unit I test? If you say yes, see section 140.

The Unit I test scores of the first-period class with the Unit II test scores of the first-period class? If you say yes, see section 144.

137   In studying the relationships of height and age in growing boys, suppose that you could select a boy of each age whose height is exactly the mean for his age group. If you then lined up these boys according to age, would the boys also be lined up according to height?

If you answer yes, then there must be a *high* degree of relationship between the two variables of height and age in growing boys.

This imaginary experiment illustrates what is meant when we say that the amount of relationship between two variables is large.

Return now to section 143 and reconsider your answer to the question.

138   You say there is a positive correlation between altitude and atmospheric pressure? Does atmospheric pressure *increase* as the altitude increases? (Such an increase in *both* would indicate a positive correlation.)

Return to section 142 and try again.

139   You say there is *no* relationship between the height and the weight of growing boys?

You will agree that, during the growth period, both height and weight increase. Perhaps you are saying that they do not increase at the same rate—that there is not a *perfect* relationship. Quite right, but the question did not specify a perfect relationship!

Return to section 135 and reconsider your answer; see where a "yes" answer takes you.

140   Although the scores made by two classes on the same test may be *similar* (with respect to class averages and spread of scores), there can be no *correlation* between them.

Why?

Because the teacher does not have *pairs* of scores.

Return to section 136, read the question again, and reconsider your answer.

141   Are you saying that there is not much relationship between the increase in height and the increase in age of growing boys?

You may return to section 143 and reconsider your answer at this point, or you may pursue this line of reasoning a bit further by turning to section 137.

142   You have said that the amount of relationship between height and age of growing boys is large. Experience tells you that it is large, yet you do not know *how* large. You have no *measure* of the degree of relationship. It is not a *perfect* relationship because some boys grow faster or slower than others of their age. But there is a relationship, a correlation.

It becomes apparent that you need some measure of the *degree* of relationship, some *coefficient* of correlation. Statisticians have developed one, and you will learn how to compute it. Before you start computing, consider further the nature of correlation.

Consider this example:

In traveling from the seashore to the high mountains, people notice a change in the atmospheric pressure. At 10,000 feet, or higher, they "run out of breath" sooner and they tire more easily than at sea level.

In comparing the changes of altitude and atmospheric pressure, will you find a relation? Of course. But of what kind? Is it a *positive* or a *negative* correlation?

If you say positive, see section 138.

If negative, section 136.

133   § **142**

143   There is, of course, some degree of relationship between height and weight of growing boys, although it is not a perfect relationship.

Height and weight do not always increase at the same rate.

If you could measure the *degree* of relationship, it might be high or it might be low.

Suppose you compare the height (only) of growing boys with their chronological age. Would you say that a measure of this *relationship* would be large or small?

If you would say "large," see section 142.

If you would say "small," see section 141.

144   Yes, of course, the teacher can compute a measure of the correlation between the scores on two different tests for the same pupils. She has a *pair* of scores for each pupil.

You should now have developed the concept of correlation: it is the relationship between two sets of connected data (or pairs of scores). It has been evident that the degree or amount of correlation is a variable quantity, that it may be large or may be small. Hence a measure or coefficient of correlation is needed.

Correlation may be positive or it may be negative. Age and height of growing boys have positive correlation; atmospheric pressure and altitude have negative correlation.

Correlation can be shown graphically in a manner that gives a visual impression of its magnitude (size) and direction (positive or negative).

To see how correlation is thus shown, proceed to section 145.

The Correlation Scattergram

145 Correlation may be shown graphically on what is called a *scattergram* or scatter diagram of the pairs of scores. For an illustration, the scores of 10 students have been chosen from their records on two tests. Here are their scores:

Student	Test I	Test II
1	43	65
2	47	78
3	36	58
4	46	70
5	38	62
6	32	53
7	41	72
8	52	76
9	34	46
10	42	64
Means	41	63

The scattergram for these scores is on the facing page.

Observe that in the headings of the scattergram, the scores are grouped. It could have been made up for the ungrouped scores, but then it would have had 21 columns and 33 rows. The scattergram of score groups is more compact and manageable, and the correlation appears more clearly.

Observe the organization of the scattergram. The scores on Test I are grouped in the seven score-size groups indicated by the column headings; the scores on Test II are grouped in the seven score-size groups indicated at the side, in the row labels or row headings. The highest score groups are farthest right and at the top; the lowest, farthest left and at the bottom. A student's scores are placed in the scattergram columns according to his score on Test I and in the scattergram rows according to his score on Test II. Thus student number 2, who made 47 on Test I, belongs in the 47-49 column; and since he made 78

TEST I

	32-34	35-37	38-40	41-43	44-46	47-49	50-52
75-79						#2	#8
70-74				#7	#4		
65-69				#1			
60-64			#5	#10			
55-59		#3					
50-54	#6						
45-49	#9						

(TEST II is the vertical axis label for the rows)

on Test II he also belongs in the 75-79 row. Do you find him? Can you find the student who scored 41 on Test I and 65 on Test II? A student's place is established by his *pair* of scores.

Using students' numbers makes it possible to locate their individual places in the scattergram, and is useful in this introduction to the concept. But ordinarily the achievements of individuals are not a matter for record in statistics, and a tally mark instead of a student's number is sufficient. It is useful, and often necessary, to locate the score groups that contain the mean scores; in this scattergram the column and the row are marked off by double lines.

Now, what can you tell about the correlation between the student's scores on the two tests? Is this correlation positive or is it negative?

If you say positive, see section 147.

If you say negative, see section 150.

146   Can't you tell whether the correlation is large or small? Do students who make high scores on Test A consistently make about the same scores on Test B, and do students who make low scores on Test A all make about the same scores on Test B? The scattergram will show that they do if the correlation is large.

Return to section 149 for another look at the scattergram, then try the question again.

147   You have said that the scattergram of test scores in section 145 shows positive correlation. You are correct. Do you see why?

Students who scored high on the first test also scored high on the second; those who were low on the first also scored low on the second test. Note that the students marks *tend* to fall along or close to a diagonal line which runs from lower left to upper right on the scattergram. (Remember that Test I score-groups must *always* run from left to right at the heads of the columns; and Test II score-groups always start at the bottom and go up.)

TEST I

		32-34	35-37	38-40	41-43	44-46	47-49	50-52
	75-79						#2	#8
	70-74				#7	#4		
	65-69				#1			
TEST II	60-64			#5	#10			
	55-59		#3					
	50-54	#6						
	45-49	#9						

Here again is scattergram of section 145. From it, what can you tell about the *amount* of correlation between scores on Tests I and II?

If you think it is small, see section 151.

If you think it is large, see section 149

If you cannot tell about the amount, see section 153.

148   You decided that the correlation is small, and you are right. The tally marks are far too scattered to indicate a high degree of correlation.

Here is one more scattergram:

Test X

	11	12	13	14	15	16	17	18	19	20	21	22
9		/	/					/				/
8	/	/		/	/	/		/		/	/	
7		/		/		/	/	/	/		/	
6	/		/	/	/	//	/	/	/	/		/
5		/			/	///		/	/		/	/
4		/		//				/	/	/		
3								/	/		/	/
2											/	

Test Y

What can you tell about the correlation between scores on Tests X and Y?

If you think it is small and positive, see section 154.

If you think it is large and negative, see section 152.

If you think it is small and negative, see section 156.

149 You are right, of course.

The closer the student marks are to the diagonal line, the larger will be the correlation.

Now, try this scattergram:

Test A

Test B	1	2	3	4	5	6	7	8	9	10
9						/		/		
8		/		/				/		/
7			/		/		/			
6		/		//	/	/	/			
5			/		//	///			/	
4		/		/	/	/				
3	/						/	/		
2		/					/			
1										

Keep in mind that each tally mark represents a *pair* of scores for one student: his score on Test A and his score on Test B.

What can you tell of the *amount* of correlation between scores on Tests A and B?

If you say it is large, see section 155.

If you say it is small, see section 148.

If you cannot tell about the amount, see section 146.

150   You missed on this one. "Negative" is not the correct answer. Why?

Recall the altitude-atmospheric pressure example. When altitude is high, atmospheric pressure is low; this example is one of negative correlation.

Look again at the pattern of scores in the scattergram and try the question once more.

Return to section 145.

151   You have said that the correlation is small. But it cannot be small.

Recall that the students who scored high on Test I also scored high on Test II, and that those who were low on Test I were also low on Test II, without exception. A small correlation would have many exceptions.

Now turn to section 147 and take another look at the scattergram; then answer the question correctly.

152   You are partly right. The correlation is clearly negative. But how can you tell whether the amount is large or small?

Return to section 149 and retrace your steps. You need something you have missed in the study of that scattergram.

153 Can't you tell whether the correlation is large or small? Take another look at the scattergram in section 147 and choose an answer.

154   Wrong.

Your choice of answer on this one suggests that you have not obtained a clear idea of *amount* and *direction* of correlation.

Return to section 145 and retract your steps.

155   If you guessed on this answer, you guessed wrong. In any event, your answer is wrong. Return to section 149 and examine the scattergram more closely; then answer the question again.

156   You have said that the scattergram shows a small and negative correlation. Will you stick by this answer or do you wish to return to section 148 for another look?

If you have made up your mind, you have examined carefully the pattern of tally marks. Those in the upper left and lower right corners predominate. Thus there is a tendency toward the scores forming a diagonal line running between those two corners; this downward direction indicates a negative correlation. But there are exceptions: a few students scored above the mean on both tests; and a few scored below the mean on both tests. Thus the negative correlation is not high, or large; it appears to be small. (Negative correlations are seldom found in test scores.)

How large or how small? These are relative terms and give no clear idea of the amount of the correlation. A measure is needed.

Continue with section 157 for further discussion of correlation.

The Coefficient of Correlation

157   Of all users of statistics, teachers especially must understand and be able to compute and interpret a correlation coefficient, because comparisons and correlations of test data are frequently reported in research and are useful in many ways.

There is, unfortunately, no *simple* way to compute a measure of correlation. Statisticians, when they work as they often do with a large number of pairs of scores, compute the coefficient of correlation, *r*, by what is known as the Pearson product-moment method. (You can find an explanation of the process in any statistics textbook or in the appendices of most tests and measurements textbooks.)

You will compute a close approximation of the Pearson *r* by an easier method. As you proceed through the computation you should gain some understanding of the nature of *r* as a measure of correlation; the computation will be given to you step by step, usually without explanation in order to keep attention on the actual work.

You have seen that a correlation may be large or small, positive or negative. It may be zero if there is no relationship between the pairs of scores. The maximum size of *r* is 1.00, hence the range of *r* is from $+1.00$ to -1.00. Note also that .90 is a large or high positive correlation and that $-.32$ is a small or low negative correlation.

The method to be presented is adequate for comparing test scores of one class, but it is cumbersome when the number of scores is large (that is, 40 or more).

Ready?

Proceed to section 159.

158 Given: In the X and Y columns below, 8 pairs of scores.

Required: to compute the coefficient of correlation between the two tests.

First, complete the x and y columns:

X	Y	x	y
32	68	3	8
24	58	− 5	− 2
28	60	− 1	0
36	65		
30	58		
25	56		
29	60		
28	55		
$Mn = 29$	$Mn = 60$		

What do you have for your last two numbers?

If you have 1 and 5, see section 169.

If you have − 1 and 5, see section 161.

If you have 1 and − 5, see section 166.

If you have − 1 and − 5, see section 163.

159 The coefficient of correlation of a small group of pairs of test scores can be computed by what is called the deviation method in five steps:

(1) Set up a table with seven columns, as described below.
(2) Compute the data for the various columns.
(3) Add each of the last three columns.
(4) Substitute the sums in the appropriate formula.
(5) Make the indicated computations.

The seven column headings are:

X: the scores on the first test
Y: the corresponding (paired) scores on the second test
x: deviation of each X score from the mean of the X scores; $+$ if the score is above the mean; $-$ if below the mean
y: deviations of Y scores from the Y mean; $+$ or $-$ as explained above
x^2: each x deviation squared; always $+$
y^2: each y deviation squared; always $+$
xy: each x deviation multiplied by its paired y deviation; watch the sign! ($- \times - = +$ and $- \times + = -$)

For an example, continue with section 158.

160   You have multiplied each x value by itself to obtain x^2 and have obtained the sum, $\Sigma x^2 = 102$. Similarly, you have obtained $\Sigma y^2 = 138$. Your sums are correct.

Now complete the last column, xy, watching carefully the signs (a $-$ number times a $-$ number $=$ a $+$ number, and a $-$ number times a $+$ number $=$ a $-$ number). After you have completed the xy column, find its sum Σxy. This sum is an algebraic sum, and to get it you add separately the $+$ values and the $-$ values, then take their total, which may be a $+$ or a $-$ number. (If you feel any uncertainty about an algebraic sum, look back to section 114.)

X	Y	x	y	x^2	y^2	xy
32	68	3	8	9	64	24
24	58	-5	-2	25	4	
28	60	-1	0	1	0	
36	65	7	5	49	25	
30	58	1	-2	1	4	
25	56	-4	-4	16	16	
29	60	0	0	0	0	
28	55	-1	-5	1	25	

$$\Sigma xy = \text{---} ? \text{---}$$

If you compute 88, see section 174.
If you compute 87, see section 162.
If you compute 92, see section 170.

161   No, you missed.

A score *above* the mean is positive; a number not marked with a sign is a positive number. A score *below* the mean is negative.

Return to section 158 and check *all* of the signs in your x and y columns.

162 You have made a small but important error.

Possibly the error is in multiplying -1 by 0. What is this product?

Or possibly your error is in addition.

Return to section 160 and try again to obtain the correct sum of the xy column.

163 Correct. Deviations of scores *below* the mean are "$-$" and you have them so marked.

All of the values in the first four columns are shown below. Now, complete the next two columns, x^2 and y^2.

X	Y	x	y	x^2	y^2
32	68	3	8	9.	64
24	58	-5	-2		
28	60	-1	0		
36	65	7	5		
30	58	1	-2		
25	56	-4	-4		
29	60	0	0		
28	55	-1	-5		
$Mn = \overline{29}$	$Mn = \overline{60}$			$\Sigma x^2 = \overline{}$	$\overline{} = \Sigma y^2$

After computing each x^2 and y^2, add the columns, obtaining the quantities Σx^2 and Σy^2.

As a check on your accuracy, which pair of sums did you obtain?

If you have 102 and 138, see section 160.

If you have 16 and 40, see section 165.

If you have 104 and 138, see section 171.

If you have any other sums, recheck your values for x, y, x^2, and y^2, and your addition.

164   Your product is incorrect. It is 12×138, not 102×138. Learn to check your answer by asking if it is reasonable.

138 times 100 would be 138 00 or 13,800. So, your product must be larger than 13,800.

Return to section 174 and again multiply Σx^2 by Σy^2.

165   Your Σx^2 and your Σy^2 are both wrong. You have apparently forgotten that a − number multiplied by a − number equals a +. number. Thus, all products in the x^2 and y^2 columns are positive numbers.

Return to section 163 and make all x^2 and y^2 values positive; then add the columns again. (Add each column at least twice, once down and once up, and add it again if the two sums do not agree.) You must obtain the correct sums before you can proceed.

166   No, you missed. A score *above* the mean is positive; a number not marked with a sign is a positive number. A score *below* the mean is negative.

Return to section 158 and check *all* of the signs in your x and y columns.

167   If you used the "exact" method of extracting the square root, you should have obtained 118.64; this may be rounded to the nearest whole number, 119, since it is so large (over 100).

If you used a slide rule, you may have had some difficulty coming closer than 119, which is satisfactory.

You began with the formula:

$$r = \frac{\Sigma xy}{\sqrt{\Sigma x^2 \times \Sigma y^2}}$$

Substitute the obtained values:

$$r = \frac{88}{\sqrt{14,076}} = \frac{88}{119}$$

It appears that r is large, but less than 1.00; r is positive, because Σxy was a positive value.

Make your division; carry it to three decimal places and round off to two.

Compare your value with section 179.

168   In using the method of approximation, you divide 14,076 by 120 (the guessed root) and obtain a quotient of 117.3. Taking the mean of 120 and 117.3 gives a square root of 118.65. (The quotient and the guess are nearly the same size, hence the obtained square root is a satisfactory approximation; you need not repeat the process.)

Since the estimated square root is large (over 100), you may as well round it off to the nearest whole number, 119.

Now turn to section 167.

169   No, you missed. A score *above* the mean is positive; a number not marked with a sign is a positive number. A score *below* the mean is negative.

Return to section 158 and check *all* of the signs in your x and y columns.

170   Your sum is incorrect. Do you have any negative values in the xy column? Did you subtract the sum of the − values from the sum of the + values?

You must have the correct values in order to compute r.

Return to section 160, find your error, and correct it.

171   Your Σx^2 sum is wrong.

Did you *square* each value of 1 or double it? ($1 \times 1 =$ — ? —)

Or, possibly your error is in addition; did you add each column down and then up until your up and down sums agreed? You must have the correct sums before proceeding.

Return to section 163, find your error, and correct it.

172   You have multiplied Σx^2 by Σy^2 and have obtained 14,076 as the product. Correct.

The next step is to obtain the square root of this value.

If you know how to obtain the square root, do so and check your answer in section 167.

If you wish to use the approximation method to obtain the square root, turn to section 175.

173
$$r = \frac{-180}{\sqrt{618 \times 1,413}}$$

Remembering the order of operations, first multiply the two numbers as indicated, and find the square root of the product.

If you know how to obtain the square root, do so and check your answer with section 183.

If you wish to use the approximation method to obtain the square root, turn to section 182.

174　You have multiplied each x value by its corresponding y value to obtain xy. Then you added the xy column to obtain $\Sigma xy = 88$. Your sum is correct. You have now obtained the three values needed to compute r, the coefficient of correlation between the X scores and the Y scores.

Substitute your values for the symbols in the formula:

$$r = \frac{\Sigma xy}{\sqrt{\Sigma x^2 \times \Sigma y^2}}$$

(Take care not to confuse the letters x or X with the multiplication sign $\times$.) Substituting:

$$r = \frac{88}{\sqrt{102 \times 138}}$$

The next order of operations is important:

First, multiply Σx^2 by Σy^2 (that is, multiply 102 by 138).
Second, find the square root of the product.
Third, divide Σxy by the square root.

To check on the first step: What is the product of Σx^2 and Σy^2?

If you say 1,656, see section 164.
If you say 14,076, see section 172.

175 To obtain the square root of 14,076 by the approximation method you proceed as you did in section 49, where you found the square root of a much smaller number. (You may want to review this section.) But because 14,076 is a big number your first guess might come far from the correct value. To avoid this difficulty, remember that if a large number is cut up into groups of two digits each (any odd digit is also a group), the number of groups shows the number of digits in the square root of that number. (A fraction may have to be added.) The groups start at the decimal point. Thus

$$14{,}076 \qquad \text{becomes} \qquad \overline{1}\ \overline{40}\ \overline{76}$$

and you perceive that $\sqrt{14{,}076}$ must have three digits, that is, must be 100 or more but less than 1,000.

Now, guess the square root of the first three digits (of 140) and multiply your guess by 10; the result will be a guess at the square root of 14,000 or 14,076. And if you remember that $12 \times 12 = 144$, which is the same as saying that $\sqrt{144} = 12$, you may very well guess at 12 for the approximate square root of 140 and 120 for the approximate square root of 14,076.

So try this guess of 120. Divide 14,076 by 120 (the guessed root); compute the mean of the quotient with 120 (the guess). Then check your result by squaring this mean. If it is too far off, take a further mean as in section 49.

When you think you have found the square root of 14,076, compare your result with that in section 168.

176   Your problem is to compute the coefficient of correlation, r, between the following 20 pairs of test scores, using the deviation method that you used for the scores in section 158.

X	Y
34	51
36	43
42	42
30	47
28	45
40	48
44	60
24	45
40	40
35	59
32	44
30	61
35	64
29	64
32	61
27	58
44	46
30	62
37	62
35	45

Set up your table for obtaining the data needed to compute r. Check this part with section 178.

177 You should have the following sums:

$\Sigma x^2 = 618.$
$\Sigma y^2 = 1413.$
$\Sigma xy = -180$ (note the $-$ sign)

If you have these exact values, proceed to section 180.

If any of your answers differ, turn to section 186 to check your work.

178   The upper part of your table should show:

X	Y	x	y	x^2	y^2	xy
34	51	0	−1	0	1	0
36	43	2	−9	4	81	−18

Complete the table, computing all values.

Note that any number multiplied by 0 equals 0.

Remember the rules for minus signs; since x and y are each squared, the values in the x^2 and y^2 columns are all positive. There are, however, some negative values in the xy column (11 of them).

Now, obtain the sums of the x^2, y^2, and xy columns. (In the xy column, this sum is algebraic. Add the + values and the − values separately; find their algebraic sum and mark it with the proper sign. This number, with its sign, is Σxy. If you need to have algebraic sums made clear, review section 114.)

Check your sums with section 177.

§ **178**   160

179 The coefficient of correlation between the results of the two tests, given in section 158, comes out to be .74. This figure for *r* indicates that there is a definite relationship between the scores on the two tests. Students who score high, medium, or low on one test *tend* also to score high, medium, or low, respectively, on the other test. The correlation is far from perfect, however. The interpretation of correlation coefficients is discussed in most statistics textbooks, if you wish this matter elaborated.

To review the steps in computing *r:*

(1) Set up a table with seven column headings: X, Y, x, y, x^2, y^2, and xy.
(2) Fill in all values in the seven columns.
(3) Find the sum of each of the last three columns: Σx^2, Σy^2, and Σxy.
(4) Substitute these sums into the formula:

$$r = \frac{\Sigma xy}{\sqrt{\Sigma x^2 \times \Sigma y^2}}$$

(5) Compute *r*.

If you have mastered the process and are ready for an assignment, turn to section 187 .

If you wish another practice run-through, turn to section 176.

180 You now have the values which are to be substituted for symbols in the formula:

$$r = \frac{\Sigma xy}{\sqrt{\Sigma x^2 \times \Sigma y^2}}$$

Substitute the values in the formula and, before making any computations, check your work in section 173.

181 The value of the correlation coefficient should be about .37.

182　　The approximation method of finding a square root was explained in section 49. You may wish to review this section.

You need now to get the square root of a large number, the product of 618 multiplied by 1,413. It is well to make an estimate of the square root before computing it in order to know whether the computed root is reasonable. The product is similar to this: xxx,xxx (it has six digits). Marking off pairs of digits leftward from the decimal point gives three groups, thus: xx xx xx. Since there are three groups, the square root will be a three-digit number, like xxx.

Now guess your square root. Since the approximation procedure provides for adjusting from the guessed root to a more nearly precise root, you can arbitrarily guess the third digit as a zero, thus: xx0; you can even guess the second and third digits as zeros, thus: x00. The mean of the guessed root and the quotient will be very close to the true square root. Complete the computation.

If you find the square root is approximately 934, go on to section 183.

If your computed square root is not approximately 934, go to section 184.

183   The product of 618 and 1,413 is 873,234. If you computed the square root (rounded off to one decimal place) by a precise method, you should have obtained 934.5.

If you estimated the square root by the approximation method, you obtained some number between 933 and 935.

You now have

$$r = \frac{-180}{\sqrt{873,234}}$$

The final step is to divide -180 by the value of the square root that you obtained.

Check your results in section 185.

184   You have either made some error in multiplying 618 by 1,413, or some error in computing the square root; or you may have computed a square root that is a satisfactory approximation and not have recognized it as satisfactory.

The product of 618 and 1,413 is 873,234. (Did you multiply correctly?) Marked off, it is 87 32 34.

If you guessed the square root of 873,234 to be 900 (by remembering that $9 \times 9 = 81$), then you divided 873,234 by 900 and obtained a quotient of 970.026, approximately 970. The mean of 970 and 900 is 935. Squaring 935 gives 874,225, which is close enough to 873,234, so 935 is a satisfactory approximate square root.

If you guessed $\sqrt{873.234}$ to be 940, your quotient should have been 926.8; the mean of 940 and this quotient is 934.4; if you square this you will find that it is a very close approximation of the true square root.

If you guessed $\sqrt{873.234}$ to be 930, your quotient should have been 939; the mean of 930 and this quotient is 934.5; if you square this you will find that it is a very close approximation of the true square root.

Other guesses may have led you to find $\sqrt{873.234} = 933$, another satisfactory approximation.

If you have computed a square root that is more than slightly below 933 or more than slightly above 935, you should return to section 182 and recompute, if possible by another method. If your computation of the square root falls in this range, it is satisfactory and you should go on to section 183.

185 $r = -.19$ (rounding off to two decimal places only). Now, what does it mean?

You have found the coefficient of correlation between two tests (which were called Test X and Y). You have a measure of the relationship between them. The value of Σxy was negative, which inevitably determined the sign of r (because Σx^2 and Σy^2, which make the denominator of the fraction, are always positive).

What does a negative coefficient of correlation tell us about the performance of students on the two tests? Do students who score high on one test tend to score high on the other test also? The sign indicates the direction of correlation.

What does the value (size) of r indicate? What are the chances of a student doing relatively as well on one test as on the other?

This review problem began with section 176.

Proceed now to the General Assignment, section 187.

X	Y	x	y	x^2	y^2	xy
34	51	0	− 1	0	1	0
36	43	2	− 9	4	81	−18
42	42	8	−10	64	100	−80
30	47	− 4	− 5	16	25	20
28	45	− 6	− 7	36	49	42
40	48	6	− 4	36	16	−24
44	60	10	8	100	64	80
24	45	−10	− 7	100	49	70
40	40	6	−12	36	144	−72
35	59	1	7	1	49	7
32	44	− 2	− 8	4	64	16
30	61	− 4	9	16	81	−36
35	64	1	12	1	144	12
29	64	− 5	12	25	144	−60
32	61	− 2	9	4	81	−18
27	58	− 7	6	49	36	−42
44	46	10	− 6	100	36	−60
30	62	− 4	10	16	100	−40
37	62	3	10	9	100	30
35	45	1	− 7	1	49	− 7

$Mn = 34$ $Mn = 52$ $\Sigma x^2 = 618$ $\Sigma y^2 = 1413$ $+277$
-457

$\Sigma xy = -180$

Correct your errors and proceed to section 180.

General Assignment

187   Compute the coefficient of correlation, *r*, of the 20 pairs of test scores given below, using the deviation method summarized in the equation:

$$r = \frac{\Sigma xy}{\sqrt{\Sigma x^2 \times \Sigma y^2}}$$

31	51
29	43
26	42
35	47
26	45
29	48
36	60
27	45
31	40
29	59
26	44
33	61
26	64
37	64
37	61
28	58
38	46
33	62
31	62
28	45
Means 31	52

Turn in your completed 7-column table and show the steps in using the formula; you need not show the actual computations.

If you wish to check your final answer, see section 181.

APPENDICES

Interpretation of Test Data

Two 50-minute statistics tests were given to a group of 52 students in a tests and measurements class.

Test A required the computation of 10 measures from given data, without notes or formulas. 50 points were possible.

Test B was a 48-item multiple-choice test of knowledge of symbols and terms and of concepts and understandings.

The results were summarized as follows:

	Test A	Test B
R	12-50	15-41
Md	45.7	30.8
Mn	42.8	30.2
σ	8.8	5.7

You can see that the mean and median scores were much higher on Test A than on Test B and that there was also a much greater spread of scores on the first test. The computation test (Test A) was the easier, as the mean score was 86% of the total points possible; the mean score on the second test (Test B) was 62% of the total possible score. Note also that on Test A the mean score is about 3 points below the median, suggesting that some very low scores pulled the mean down.

The highest score of Test A is less than 1σ above the mean, while the lowest score is 3.5σ below the mean; apparently most of the scores were relatively high and a few scores were very low. On Test B, the highest score was nearly 2σ above the mean and the lowest score was more than $2\frac{1}{2}\sigma$ below the mean; these facts, together with the smaller standard deviation, suggest that the scores tended to pile up closer to the median than was the case in Test A.

The correlation between the two sets of tests scores was .36, which is low and positive. It appears that many students did not rank the same on Test B as they did on Test A: they scored either higher or lower. The low correlation suggests that the two tests measure different kinds of skills or abilities; that some

171

students are better at computation while others excel in interpreting verbal test items.

Because performance on the two tests was not equivalent, a raw score on one test is not comparable to the same score on the other test. A student cannot compare his relative *performance* on the two tests by comparing his raw scores alone. For example, a score of 30 on Test B is "average" or at the mean; on Test A a score of 30 is about $1\frac{1}{2}\sigma$ below the mean. In order to compare individual scores, it is necessary to convert the raw scores into some type of derived scores which represent performance relative to the average and to the spread of scores of the class as a whole. The types of derived scores and their computation and interpretation are discussed in textbooks on educational measurement. Comparisons of the raw scores of Tests A and B and one type of standard score are illustrated below. (T scores have an arbitrarily selected mean of 50 and standard deviation of 10.)

	-3σ	-2σ	-1σ	*Mn* 0	$+1\sigma$	$+2\sigma$	$+3\sigma$
A	16	25	34	43	51		
B	13	19	25	30	36	42	
T	20	30	40	50	60	70	80

From the chart we can see that a score of 50 on Test A is equivalent to about 35 on Test B and each would be assigned a T score of 58. A score of 34 on Test A is comparable to 25 on Test B and each would receive a T score of 40. T scores can be combined or averaged to determine an individual's performance on the two (or more) tests.

Before using the data (for grading purposes), more should be known of the measuring instruments. Is Test A a "good" measure of skill in computing statistics? Does Test B really measure statistical knowledge, concepts, and understandings? The data do not give any indication of the *validity* or truthfulness of the tests. Similarly, the *reliability* or consistency of measurement is not indicated by the descriptive data. To the extent to which the tests lack consistency, the individual scores are subject to error; any score may be too high or too low. One cannot tell which of the two tests is the more reliable and would be the fairer basis for grading. One must go further into statistics to be able to interpret the data properly. The brief bibliography which follows includes books which explain interpretation or statistical inference. However, the statistics given above serve to describe or summarize the performance of 52 students on two tests of achievement. This service is the function of descriptive statistics.

A Few Useful References

ARKIN, HERBERT, AND RAYMOND R. COLTON. *Tables for Statisticians.* Barnes and Noble, 1950. 152 pages, paper. Square roots and 24 other tables, each with directions for use.

BLOMMERS, PAUL, AND E. F. LINDQUIST. *Elementary Statistical Methods in Psychology and Education.* Houghton Mifflin, 1960. 528 pages. Study manual, 247 pages. Explores in depth a limited number of basic concepts and techniques, stressing the importance of a critical evaluative attitude.

DIXON, WILFRED J., AND FRANK J. MASSEY, JR. *Introduction to Statistical Analysis.* McGraw-Hill, 1951. 370 pages. Requires a minimum of mathematics and contains examples from many fields.

DOWNIE, N. M., AND R. W. HEATH. *Basic Statistical Methods,* Harper & Brothers, 1959. 235 pages, 13 tables. Stresses computation, application, and interpretation. Includes statistical inference, tests of significance, and test analysis.

HUFF, DARRELL. *How to Lie with Statistics.* Norton, 1954. 142 pages, paper. Many instances of "bumbling and chicanery" illustrate misuse of statistics. A fascinating and necessary book to balance statistics with common sense.

HUNTSBERGER, DAVID V. *Elements of Statistical Inference.* Allyn and Bacon, 1961. 248 pages, 9 tables. Brief treatment of descriptive measures, probability, and sampling, with emphasis upon interpretation in terms of probability statements.

MANUEL, HERSCHEL T. *Statistics in Measurement.* American Book Company, 1960. Simplified treatment which emphasizes meanings rather than computational skills.

Summary and Formulas

Measures of Central Tendency

THE MEAN: With small samples (or a calculator), add the individual scores and divide by the number of scores.

With scores grouped in a frequency distribution:

$$Mn = AMn + \left(i \times \frac{\Sigma fd}{N} \right)$$

THE MEDIAN OR MID-POINT: With small samples (scores in order of size), count up half-way to the middle score or half-way between the two scores in the middle.

In a frequency distribution, count up half-way by adding score frequencies; determine the lower limit (or dividing line) of the score-group containing the median, and add the necessary correction. (Example in section 89.)

THE MODE: The mode is the score which occurs with the greatest frequency; if not well defined, it is of no value and should not be reported. It cannot be determined from grouped scores.

Measures of Dispersion or Spread

THE RANGE: The difference between the highest score and the lowest score, plus one. Based on the two most extreme scores; unreliable.

QUARTILE DEVIATION OR SEMI-INTERQUARTILE RANGE

$$Q = \frac{Q_3 - Q_1}{2}$$

Q_3 is the point which separates the highest fourth from the rest of the scores; Q_1 is the point which separates the lowest fourth from the rest of the scores; both are determined by a counting process similar to that used in computing the median in a frequency distribution. (Illustrated in section 98 and section 101.)

177

STANDARD DEVIATION: With ungrouped data:

$$\sigma = \sqrt{\frac{\Sigma d^2}{N}}$$

With grouped data:

$$\sigma = i\sqrt{\frac{\Sigma fd^2}{N} - \left(\frac{\Sigma fd}{N}\right)^2}$$

Measure of Relationship

COEFFICIENT OF CORRELATION (deviation method):

$$r = \frac{\Sigma xy}{\sqrt{\Sigma x^2 \times \Sigma y^2}}$$